IF WARDS COULD TALK

To. OUR DEAR FRIEND BETTY,

WITH LOVE AND BEST WISHES.

FROM ANGELA AND DERRICK.

HAPPY MEMORIES.

" OUR SET "
Pages 7 - 8 - 9
75
117

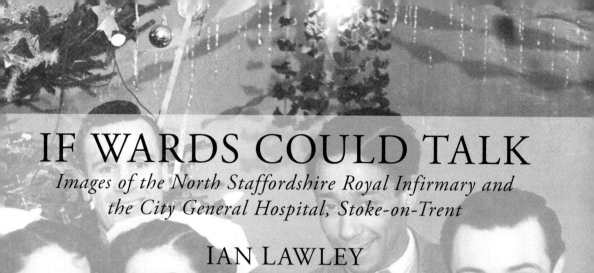

IF WARDS COULD TALK

*Images of the North Staffordshire Royal Infirmary and
the City General Hospital, Stoke-on-Trent*

IAN LAWLEY

Phillimore

CIGARETTES

2011

Published by
PHILLIMORE & CO. LTD
Healey House, Andover, Hampshire

ISBN 978-1-86077-729-5

Printed and bound in Great Britain

Manufacturing managed by
Jellfish Print Solutions

Contents

Acknowledgements

If Wards Could Talk would like to thank all the many people who have contributed to this project. In particular we would like to thank the following for their kind permission to use their photographs in this book.

Ron Alcock, Mrs P. Averill, Frank Baggaley, Gladys Ball, Ellie Bell, Gill Berrisford, A. Bissell, Linda Bratt, Dr David Brookfield, R.D. Brough, Cynthia Cadman, Jean Charsley, Frank Cooper, Pauline Dasgupta, Dr Alun Davies, Sheila Eaton, Christine Edwards, Audrey Feazey, Judith Fenton, Mrs M. Foddy, Peggy Grocott, Ann Hales, Mrs A. Hassall, Mrs I. Hassall, Mrs K. Hawley, Ann Hodgkins, Judy Hyde, Dorothy James, Bernice Kontic, Wenche Lally, Joan Leach, Joy Low, Pam Moore, Vivienne Noake, Mrs J. Oakes, Fred Owen, Brenda Potts, Tom Rhodes, Vera Schemilt, Prem and Margaret Seewoosaha, Marjorie Shingler, Mrs Smith, Chris Sylvester, Erma Taylor, James Wilkinson, Mrs Williams, Kathleen Woodward, Jim and Audrey Worgan, the North Staffordshire Medical Institute, the Nursing History Group, the Potteries Museum and Art Gallery, and the *Sentinel* newspaper.

We would also like to thank the following people for providing information and sharing their stories: Angela Davies, Eunice Bedson, Mr Bridgwood, Selwyn Brown, Mr V. Byatt, Jeanette Cooper, Rosemary Eaglen, Constance Fildes, Deidre Gossington, Alice Mary Hassall, Sylvia Keay, Mary Laird, Paddy O'Sullivan, Myrtle Summerly, Jane Walker, Barbara Walsh, Tony Wilkes, Mrs Young.

I would also like to thank Fiona Jones, Ruth Conroy, Andy Ashcroft, and Laura Breen for their support and Kate Lawley for her patience.

If Wards Could Talk was set up by the University Hospital of North Staffordshire NHS Trust with the support of the Heritage Lottery Fund.

This book is dedicated to hospital staff past and present who have served the public so well.

University Hospital of NHS
North Staffordshire
NHS Trust

heritage lottery fund
LOTTERY FUNDED

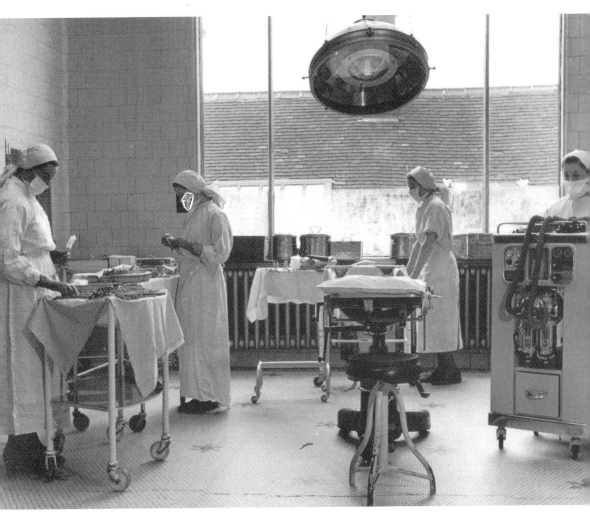

Nurses prepare the NSRI theatre for surgery, 1951.

Introduction

Stoke-on-Trent's hospitals have a long history. Remains of a medieval hospital have been found at the City General site, which also includes the former Stoke and Wolstanton parish workhouse buildings. One of these had been used as a hospital for the 'physically infirm' since the 1840s, and another was built as a lunatic asylum. The nearby North Staffordshire Royal Infirmary at Hartshill, which opened in 1869, was one of the first English hospitals to be built on the pavilion system favoured by Florence Nightingale.

As the new University Hospital of North Staffordshire takes shape and these familiar landmarks become part of history, *If Wards Could Talk*, a people's history project, has been recording the stories of staff and patients.

The idea for the project arose as a result of conversations with former staff and others who were keen to keep their memories of North Staffordshire's hospitals alive at a time of rapid change. Various individuals, including former nurses, doctors and other staff, have acted as unofficial historians, collecting images, information and memorabilia. When groups of retired nurses meet, conversation naturally turns to shared experiences and old colleagues bring photographs and press cuttings to prompt discussion. They are proud to be a part of the hospitals' history and keen to pass on their stories for future generations to enjoy. As the local healthcare environment is transformed, it is important that we celebrate and record the area's medical history and heritage.

An archive of unusual and personal memories of daily life in North Staffordshire's hospitals has now been created which offers an insight into their history and the development of the NHS that cannot be gained from documentary records. The project also set out to collect photographs which show the impact of changing patterns of healthcare on individual people and their families in the Potteries during the second half of the 20th century. These form the basis of this book.

Before the widespread use of antibiotics to treat infection, hospital stays were often quite long. Miners with severe spinal injuries and patients with illnesses such as TB could be separated from their families for months while they recuperated. Some patients faced a succession of operations for conditions that can now be treated with medicines. Both they and their carers have vivid memories of their experience. Former child patients talk fondly of the old Cheetham's Block, which had four sections: Boys, Girls, Babies and Toddlers. One lady recalled eating minced meat for the first time in her life as a patient there in the 1930s. Another former patient remembers watching a firework display through the windows and longing to play on a rocking horse that was in the ward. Others found themselves placed in adult wards so that older patients could keep an eye on them. One girl who was treated for an ear infection in the 1930s remembers learning a song:

> Here comes the nurse with a red hot poultice,
> Slaps it on and takes no notice
> Oh! Says the patient, that's far too hot,
> Oh, says the nurse, I'm sure it's not

Many nurses spoke in great detail about their three years' training. Student nurses lived on the hospital premises and many close friendships were formed. Some of the girls came from other parts of the country, or from overseas. The Home Sister looked after them, in the words of an Irish nurse, 'with the love and care of a mother. If we were sick, she nursed us, especially the girls far from home.' Although male visitors to the Nurses' Home were strictly forbidden, romance often blossomed, and nurses married doctors or other medical staff. Male nurses weren't accepted too readily to begin with. One recalled that, during his time as a student, the Theatre Sister 'always had to have a whipping boy and for three months it was me. She gave me hell.' A nurse at the City General thought that Matron 'didn't approve of men in general'. She recalled an incident when a male student nurse was sent to clean a statue of Our Lady in the church as punishment for some misdemeanour. To compound matters, he managed to break one of the statue's hands.

The rivalry between the two major hospitals is also frequently mentioned. 'It was them and us,' reminisced one City General nurse. 'We referred to them as the cottage hospital on the hill. They called us the workhouse – and our changing rooms were actually the old baths, the wash area of the workhouse.' When the two hospitals merged in 1973, some felt that they had lost their identity. 'When we lost our infirmary badge, which we had all been very proud of, somehow the Infirmary lost its personality.'

Some common themes recur in the memories of both patients and staff – hospital discipline and cleanliness, the fact that nothing was disposable, the experience of Christmas on the wards, for example. People speak of 'being in awe of Matron' and the following observations are typical. 'Matron knew exactly what was going on in every corner of the hospital. She was very astute, very, very kindly to the patients, but beds had to be exactly in line. Everything had to be spot on.' 'Discipline was very strict. Hair had to be up and under your cap. No Christian

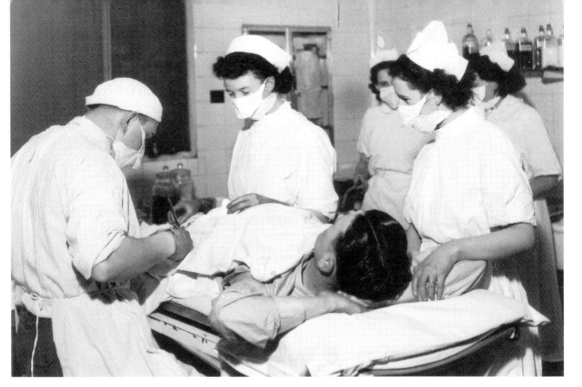

Nurses assist as a surgeon performs a procedure in theatre, 1950s.

names were allowed on the wards. No nail varnish, no jewellery, no rings, earrings, necklaces.' Many talk wistfully of the cleaning regime. 'Every morning, the first thing I did when I came on duty', recalled one Orderly, 'was pull out all the beds into the centre of the ward, sweep the floor behind them and clean it thoroughly, push them back again, do the lockers and make sure all the wheels were absolutely in order.' A junior nurse's duties included cleaning the ward and sluice, washing bedpans and sputum mugs, sterilising instruments, testing syringes for sharpness, making swabs, laying out trays and trolleys and treating patients' backs to prevent bed sores.

At Christmas the wards were decorated, and nurses went carol singing with the red lining of their capes worn on the outside to give a festive look. Ward Sisters were expected to stay on duty, and consultants came in and carved the turkeys for the patients. Staff organised concerts, pantomimes and dances.

Few people in North Staffordshire will not feel some connection with its hospitals. Around a quarter of a million people first saw the light of day in the old Maternity block, which was demolished in 2009. The University Hospital receives over 650,000 patient visits each year. More than 100 people have contributed to *If Wards Could Talk* with stories that reveal compassion, fortitude and humour in the face of illness and suffering. This book brings together some of their fascinating photographs, which give an often moving insight into the realities of hospital life.

Ian Lawley, August 2011

ONE

A Wonderful Three Years

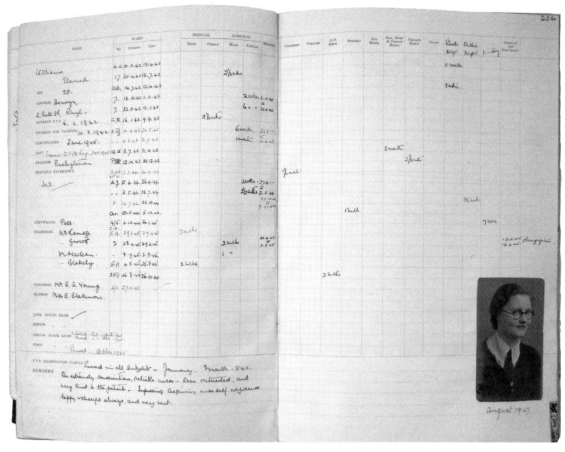

Above: Page from the Infirmary Nurses' Register. Nurses trained for three years before qualifying and were monitored closely. 'The Ward Sister had to record your progress in a book. She gave you a tick if she thought you were proficient to carry out a procedure but a cross when she felt that you couldn't. Then you took that book to Sister Tutor and she'd go through it to see how many ticks and crosses you'd got. If you hadn't got enough ticks you got told off.'

Trainee nurses in their uniforms at the Infirmary, 1937. Kathleen Woodward remembers having to provide her own uniform for the first three months of training.

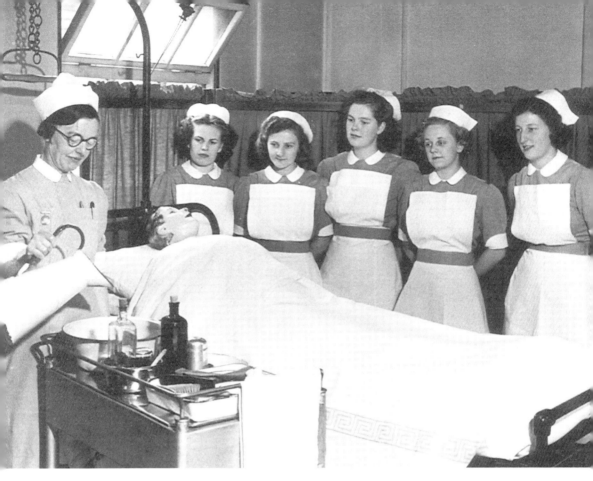

Above: Tutor Sister Wardle gives instruction in bed-washing to Preliminary Training School students at the Infirmary, 1951. The trainees named the dummy 'Mrs Mac.' One recalls, 'It's never the same when it's a real person, I can assure you. You need to have a conversation with your patient.'

Nurse M.L. Beadle in training uniform. She began training in October 1959 after working in the wage office at Beswick's pottery. Her mother and sister were both nurses and her father worked at the City General.

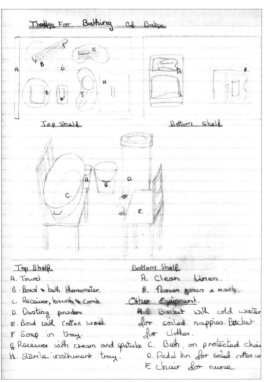

Above: 'Trolley for bathing of baby'. A page from trainee nurse Cynthia Whitfield's exercise book, *c.*1961. Laying out trays and trolleys was an important part of a junior nurse's work.

Left: Preliminary Training School class, 1951. Sister Whiteside, the tutor, stands at the back. Students spent three months in the classroom before going onto the wards for practical experience. The course followed the Syllabus of the General Trained Nurse, laid down by the General Nursing Council for England and Wales.

Right: 'Hospital corners', *c.*1950. A former student nurse recalled, 'I had to make one side of beds with the senior night nurse and then we had to pull all the beds out to the centre of the ward, dust behind, push them back again, do the lockers and make sure all the wheels were absolutely in order.'

Below: Trainee nurses in the library, Prince Henry Hall, 1951. This was part of the extension to the Nurses' Home built in 1927.

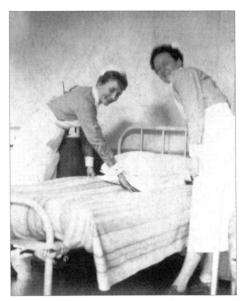

Joan Wooldridge, Staff Nurse Foden, Ken Fernyhough and Staff Nurse Fox in the Infirmary Plaster Room, 1955. Many young women gained experience as auxiliary nurses before they reached their 18th birthday and could take up formal training. Joan Wooldridge remembers her time as a pre-nursing student on the Plaster Room as 'a good introduction to nursing. The staff taught me a lot.'

Far right: Student nurses Wendy Keys, Mary Oakes, Ann Tyler, Helen Couzens in the Infirmary grounds, 1958.

Right: Preliminary Training School 'set' of 1956, group photo taken at time of qualification, 1959. Many lasting friendships were made during the three years of training.

Below: Infirmary nursing students on the balcony at the Nurses' Home, May 1956. Joan Wooldridge is second from left, back row.

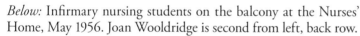

Top left: Third-year Infirmary students, with Sister Erma Clarke, NSRI, 1958. Sister Clarke was one of North Staffordshire's first West Indian nurses.

Centre left: Trainee nurses with Sister R.A. Greally, City General Hospital, 1950s. Until the two hospitals merged in 1973, each ran its own training programme.

Above: Prize-giving, City General Hospital, October 1950. Ernest Terence (Tom) Byatt is presented with the gold medal by Alderman Percy Williams, Chairman of the Stoke-on-Trent Hospital Management Committee. This was the first time that a male nurse (still something of a rarity) had come top of the set. Also pictured is silver prize winner Elsie Elizabeth Knight.

Bottom left: Prize-giving, Infirmary, April 1961. Newly qualified nurses, hospital staff and the Bishop of Stafford pose for the camera following the presentation in Prince Henry Hall. Gold medallist Derek Langston is on the far right.

Silver medallist Gill Berrisford, Gold medallist Ann Neary and Bronze medallist Catherine Manning, City General Hospital 1964. Unusually, Gill Berrisford had begun her training in Birmingham, but transferred to the City General. She recalls: 'It was brilliant, it really was, it was a wonderful three years.

Reg. No. 225261

𝕴t is hereby 𝕮ertified that

Rachel Doreen Brough

was admitted to the General part of the Register maintained by the General Nursing Council for England and Wales, on

25th April 1955

and that she is entitled in pursuance of the Nurses Acts, 1919 to 1949, to take and use the title of "Registered Nurse."

Dorothy. M. Smith. SRN.
Chairman of Council.

The Seal of the Council was hereunto affixed this 31st day of May 1955.

M. Henry. SRN.
Registrar.

Above: General Nursing Council Examination registration card, 1966. Any student arriving for the exam without a card would be refused entry.

Left: State Registered Nursing certificate awarded to Rachel Doreen Brough, 1955.

Prize giving, Infirmary, April 1966. Second-year student Linda Joan Hodgkinson (front row, centre) was awarded the Dr J.S. Hamilton prize for Proficiency in Public Health. She holds a copy of *The Mothering of Young Children*.

We hereby certify that

Joan Mary Wooldridge

completed to the satisfaction of the Committee

3 years training as a Student Nurse at the North Staffordshire Royal Infirmary (in accordance with the Regulations of the General Nursing Council for England and Wales) on .... **12 - 6 - 19 59**

1 st. Place in Medicine

Chairman Nursing Committee

Matron

In testimony of the foregoing the Corporate Seal of the Stoke-on-Trent Hospital Management Committee was hereunto affixed on the ....4th... day of ......May...... 1942.

V/ Chairman of the H.M. Committee

Secretary of the Committee

Above: Graduation certificate issued by Stoke-on-Trent Hospital Management Committee. Joan Wooldridge achieved first place in medicine in her final examination.

Below: Invitation to prize giving presentation, May 1968. By now, the School of Nursing had been joined by the School of Radiography.

NORTH STAFFORDSHIRE ROYAL INFIRMARY

SCHOOLS OF NURSING
and the
NORTH STAFFORDSHIRE
SCHOOL OF RADIOGRAPHY

The pleasure of your company is requested on the occasion of the

Annual Presentation

of Awards and Certificates

to be held in
PRINCE HENRY HALL, NURSES' HOME
on
Wednesday 15th May, 1968, at 7-30 p.m.

Mr. J. S. RAMAGE, F.R.C.S.
will make the presentations and address the nurses

R.S.V.P. on the
attached form by
1st May

Above: Group of Radiography students in light-hearted mood, 1962. Tom Rhodes (far right) was the first male student on the course. He recalls, 'Our set of trainees became quite close-knit. They were a really good bunch. But they used to hide my clothes after I had been in theatre so I couldn't find them'.

Right: Radiography students posing among the screens, 1962. Tom Rhodes remembers that this photograph was taken one Saturday morning when the students were supposed to be photographing equipment.

Below: Infirmary student nurses Agatha Kang, Soo Khoo, and George Castleldine, competing for the Marian Agnes Gullan trophy, 1966. This was a national competition for nursing students named after the author of *The Theory & Practice of Nursing*. The Infirmary team reached the final.

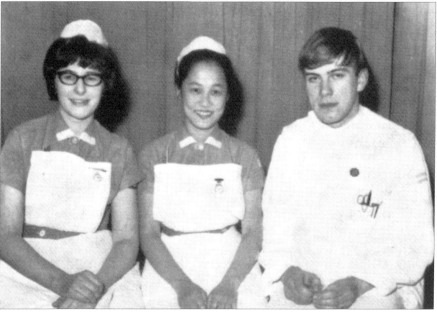

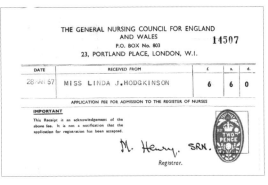

General Nursing Council Uniform Permit issued to Linda Hodgkinson, 1967. This gave the holder permission to buy the approved uniform from authorised suppliers.

Receipt for Nursing Register application fee, 1967. At the time, newly qualified nurses were obliged to pay six guineas for entry onto the Register of Nurses.

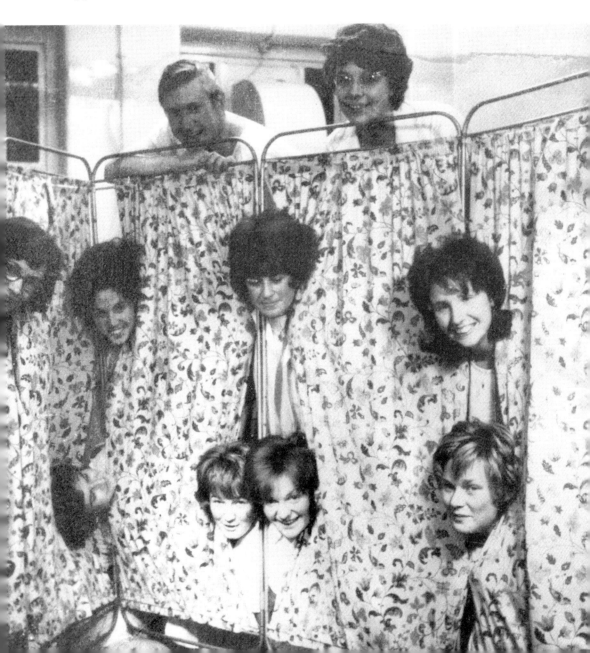

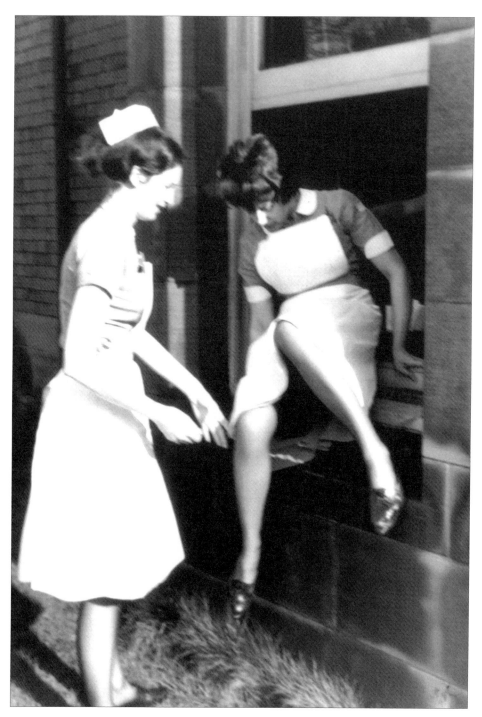

A nurse climbs out of a window at the Infirmary Nurses' Home. A nurse who trained in the 1960s recalled, 'You had to live in the Nurses' Home, and they were quite strict on the hours. However, some of us managed to find a way in where we shouldn't have done.'

TWO

Wards and Theatres

Above: Infirmary operating theatre, 1926. The theatre nursing staff and anaesthetist pose around the operating table and trolley, on which can be seen Shipway's Warm Ether Apparatus.

Left: Nurses and a patient in one of the wards at the London Road Hospital (later known as the City General), *c.*1925.

Right: Ward 9, North Staffordshire Infirmary, *c.*1925. Little in its appearance had changed since the late Victorian period. A porcelain washstand can be seen in the centre of the ward and there is a large ceramic jardinière towards the back on the right.

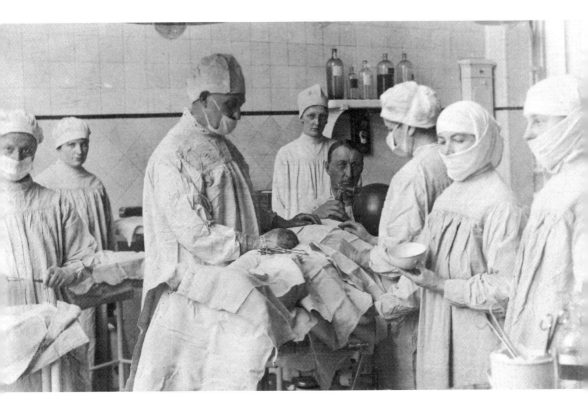

Above: Infirmary operating theatre, 1930s. Pictured are the surgeon Mr R. Alcock, the anaesthetist Dr Mott and theatre nursing staff.

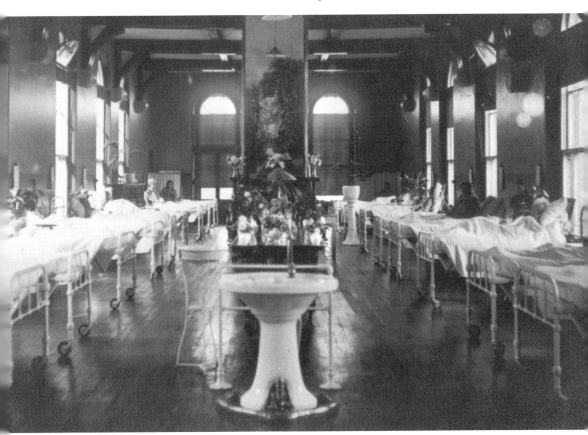

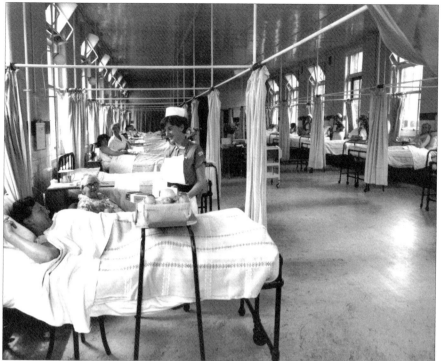

Above: The Henry Johnson Ward, North Staffordshire Infirmary, *c.*1950. This was the first ward in the hospital to have curtains around the beds.

Right: Patients and nurses in the Henry Johnson Ward, *c.*1950. Children were not allowed in the ward, but a patient's daughter remembers the Ward Sister opening the fire escape door to allow her to talk to her mother.

Below: Dr Binnie and Mr Keates (gynaecological registrar) consults with colleagues on a ward round, 1950s. 'When there was a doctor's round there had to be absolute silence,' recalled one nurse who trained in the 1950s. 'The doctors would go round each patient with the ward sister and the student nurses. We couldn't do any cleaning or serve meals, nothing at all, everybody had to line up and be with the doctor on his rounds'.

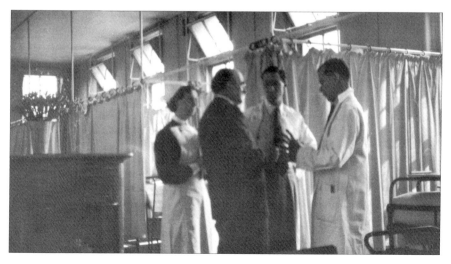

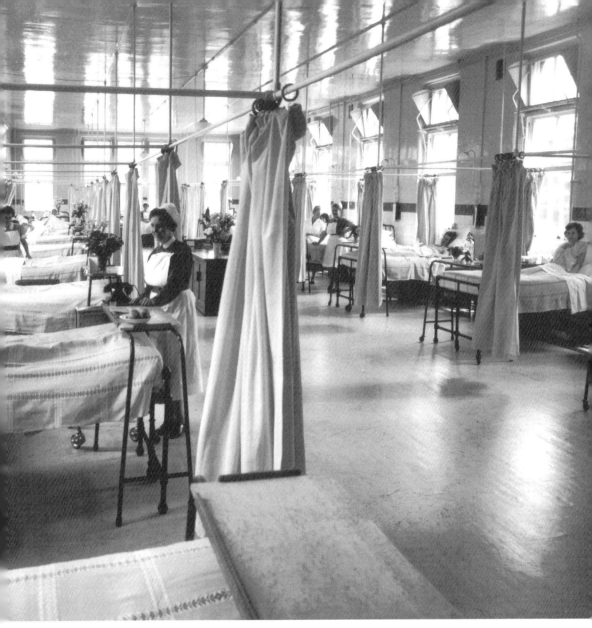

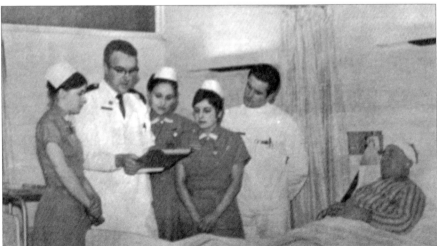

Right: A senior nurse and colleagues discuss a patient's post-operative progress, mid-1960s.

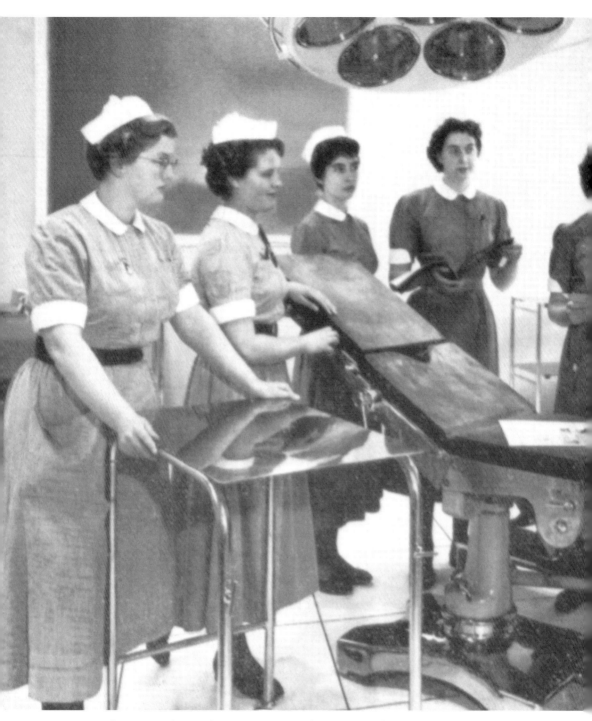

Above: Eric Short, Theatre Superintendent, with Infirmary theatre staff, *c.*1965.

Top right: Theatre Sister R.A. Greally (centre) and a group of nurses, in one of the theatres, City General Hospital.

Centre right: In the theatre, mid-1960s. The mask worn by the surgeon on the right only covers his mouth. When this happened colleagues would joking ask whether he had a 'sterile nose'.

Below right: Staff at the City General attend to a patient, 1950s. They are possibly changing a dressing.

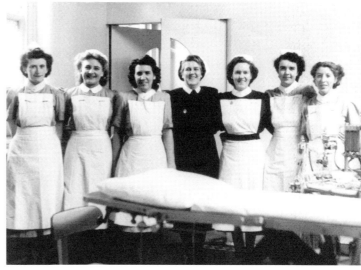

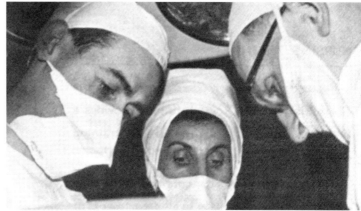

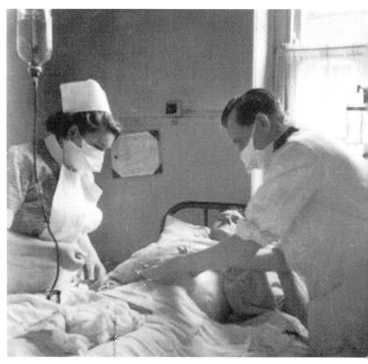

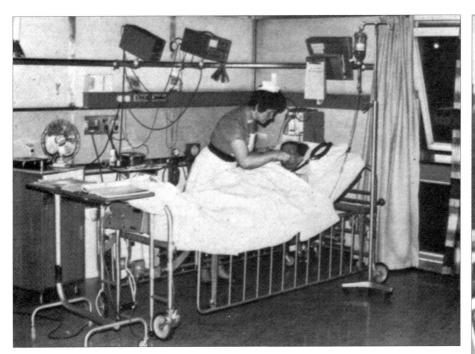

Above: Intensive Care Unit, Infirmary, mid-1960s. Prior to the creation of dedicated intensive care facilities, critically ill patients were nursed on open wards.

A patient receives care in the new renal unit, mid-1960s.

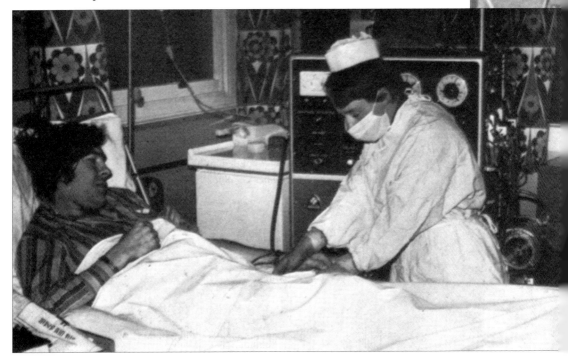

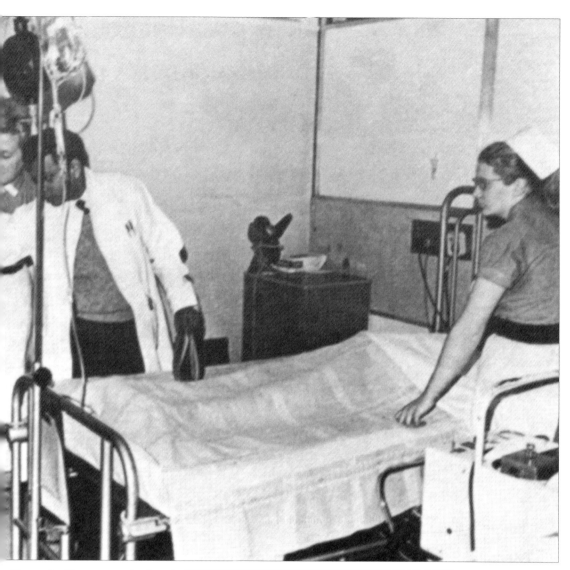

Above: Staff prepare a bed and monitoring equipment to receive a patient.

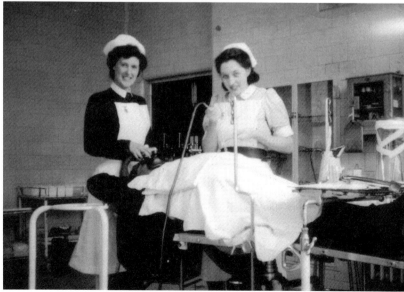

A light-hearted moment as consultant anaesthetist Dr E. Isaacson, under the blanket, pretends to be ready for surgery. Theatre Sister Litherland administers' the anaesthetic while Nurse Galloway prepares to 'operate'.

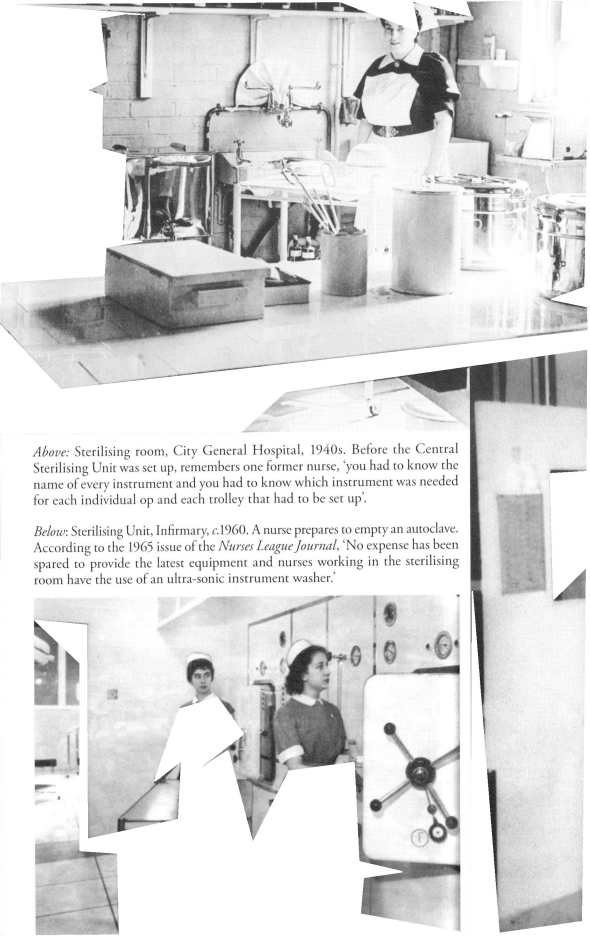

Above: Sterilising room, City General Hospital, 1940s. Before the Central Sterilising Unit was set up, remembers one former nurse, 'you had to know the name of every instrument and you had to know which instrument was needed for each individual op and each trolley that had to be set up'.

Below: Sterilising Unit, Infirmary, *c.*1960. A nurse prepares to empty an autoclave. According to the 1965 issue of the *Nurses League Journal*, 'No expense has been spared to provide the latest equipment and nurses working in the sterilising room have the use of an ultra-sonic instrument washer.'

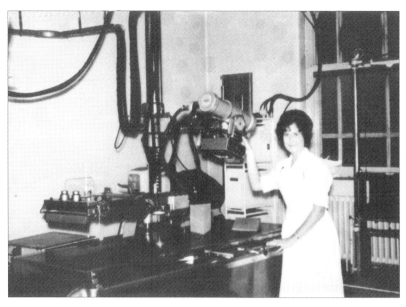

Left and below: The X-Ray room in the Radiography Department, Infirmary, 1962. An X-Ray department had opened in 1927, followed by the Radiology department in the 1930s.

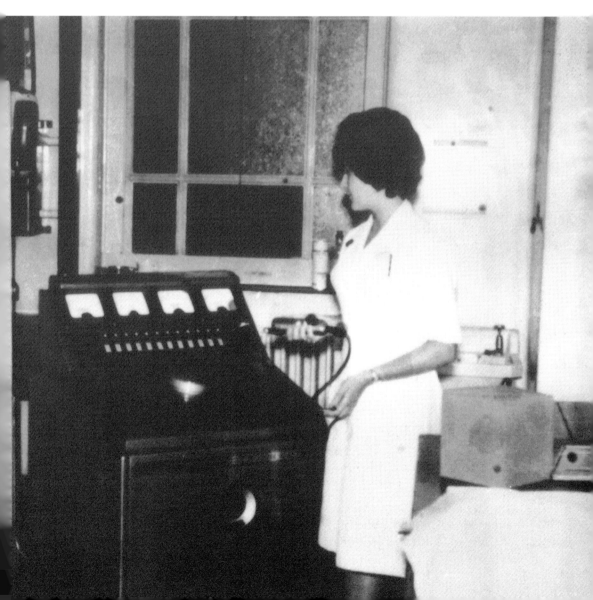

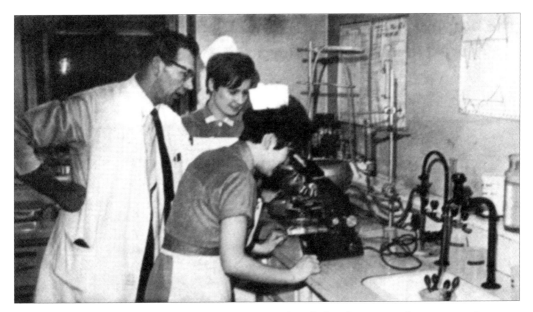

The Pathology Laboratory, mid-1960s. A consultant's daughter remembers visiting the Path Lab as a very small child in the 1940s to feed the white mice in their cages. To her the mice were pets, as she had no idea that they were used for experiments.

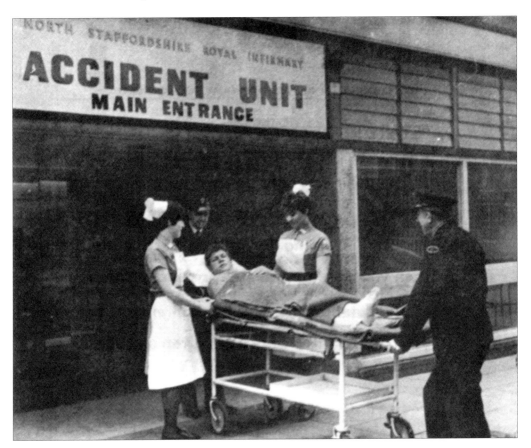

The Accident Unit, 1965. The automatic doors at the new accident unit had teething problems. They opened when the porter passed a sensor but closed before they had finished carrying the stretchers and trolleys through the doors.

THREE

From Here to Maternity

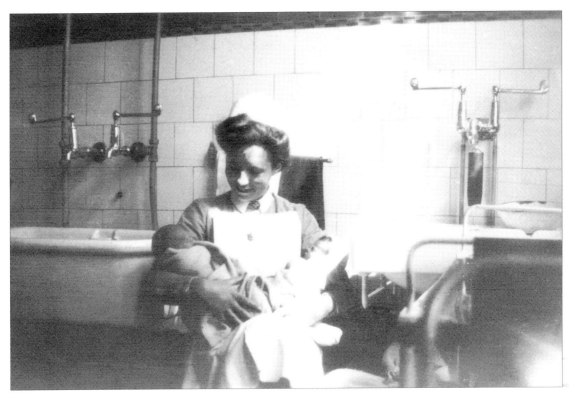

Maternity Ward, 1940s. A nurse cradles two newborn babies. Many nurses undertook midwifery training after becoming an S.R.N.

Sister Talley and colleagues pose with two young babies on the Maternity Ward balcony.

Ward sisters and staff nurses on the Henry Johnson Ward pose with proud parents (a doctor and his wife) and their baby, as they get ready to leave.

A Dutch nursing sister, who came to the UK in 1948 to gain experience of an English hospital, poses with a baby on the ward balcony. 'I felt very privileged to care for babies and work as part of the team', said one former nurse.

Ward Sisters and nurse with a newborn baby, Henry Johnson Ward.

Nurses Sheila Gale and Pauline Dawson with baby Christina Onilogbo, August 1964. When Pauline was married and had her own children, she made sure they too were born on the Henry Johnson Ward.

A successful outcome. A nurse holds the baby as the parents wait to take their new family member home.

Gas and air was commonly used to help manage the pain of childbirth.

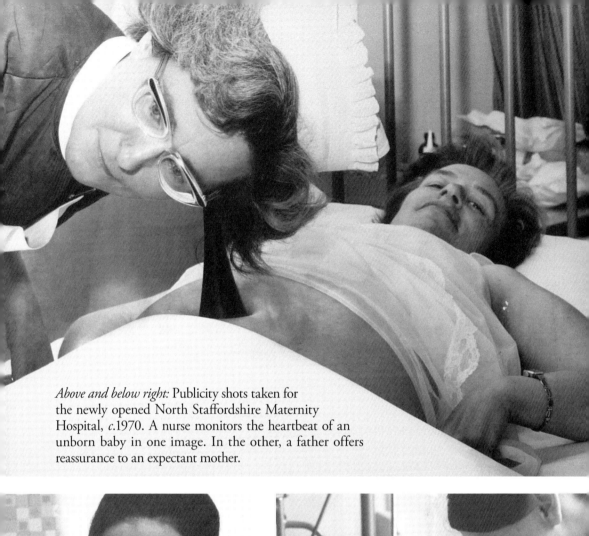

Above and below right: Publicity shots taken for the newly opened North Staffordshire Maternity Hospital, *c.*1970. A nurse monitors the heartbeat of an unborn baby in one image. In the other, a father offers reassurance to an expectant mother.

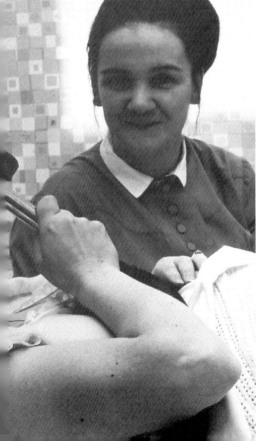

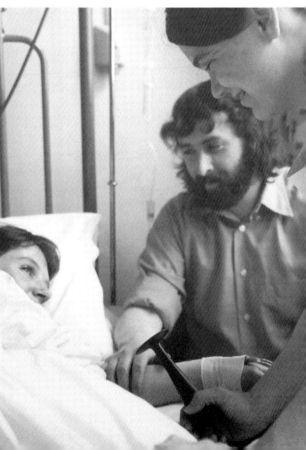

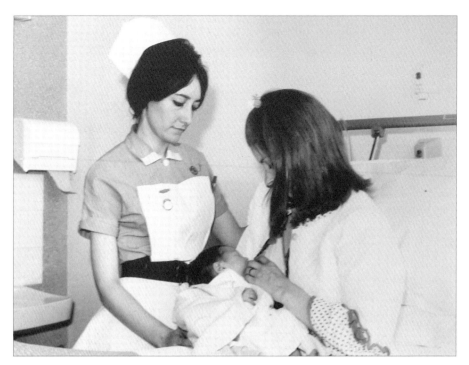

A mother nurses her newborn baby. More and more births took place in hospital in the post-war period. By 1980 99 per cent of births in North Staffordshire took place in hospital and the obstetric unit had become the second largest in the country.

Mothers rest in bed in the Maternity Ward, *c*.1970.

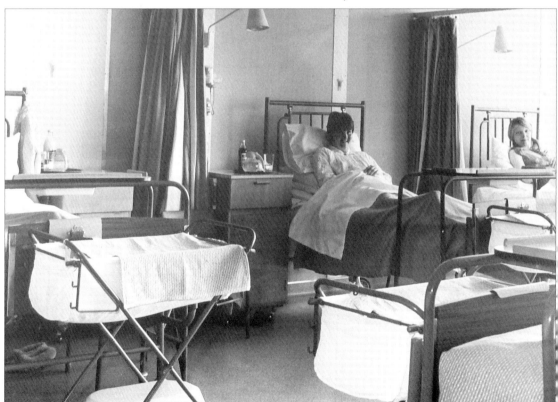

Above: Preparing milk for the babies in the milk kitchen. There were two full-time auxiliary members of staff.

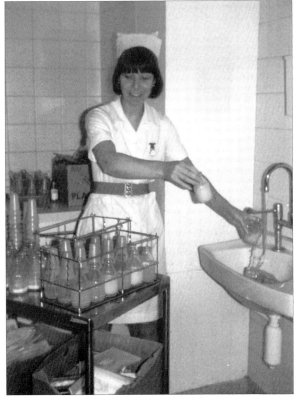

Chris Sylvester in the 'dirty milk kitchen'.

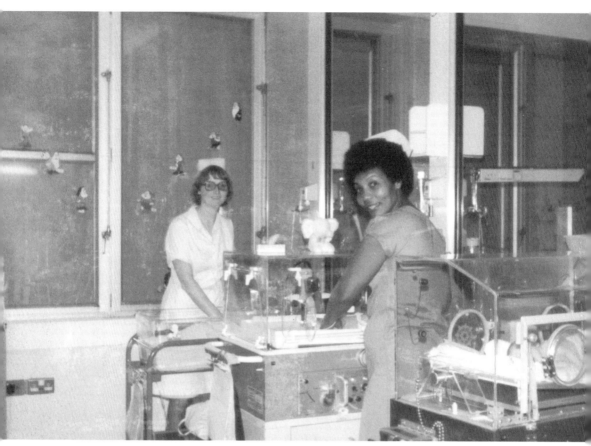

Top: Pat Johnson (nursery nurse) and Candy Smith (auxiliary nurse) at work in the Neonatal Unit. The care of premature and sick newborn babies improved steadily after the opening of the Special Care Baby Unit in 1967. Perinatal and neonatal mortality rates fell by half between 1971 and 1981, which was a greater reduction than the national average.

Above: The North Staffordshire Maternity Hospital, shortly before demolition in 2009.

Right: Nurse Pam Moore and patient chat in the Neonatal Family Unit, 1986.

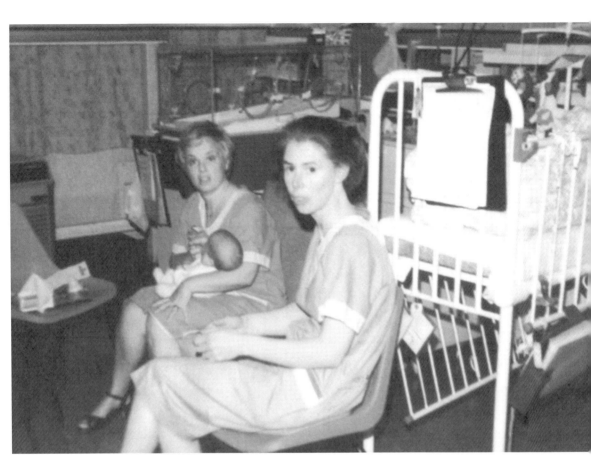

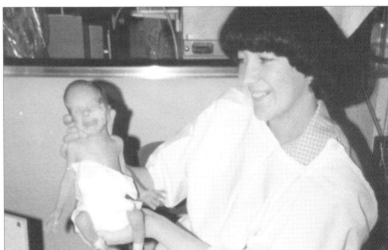

Top: Marian Booth (holding baby) and Vivien Shackley at the Neonatal Unit, 1991. The neonatal mortality rate fell by half during the 1970s. In 1971 around two babies died each week. By 1981 this had fallen to one a week. Most of these babies had been born prematurely.

Above: Nursery Nurse Judy Hyde with patient, Neonatal Unit. Intensive care for babies was introduced in the hospital in 1978 when neonatal ventilators were acquired. Before then continuous positive airways pressure machines and an early ventilator had been used for managing premature babies.

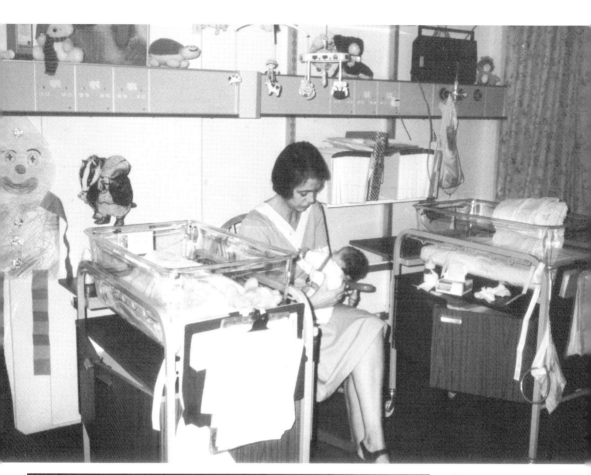

Above: Nursery nurse Jayne Robinson and baby in the Neonatal Unit, Christmas 1993.

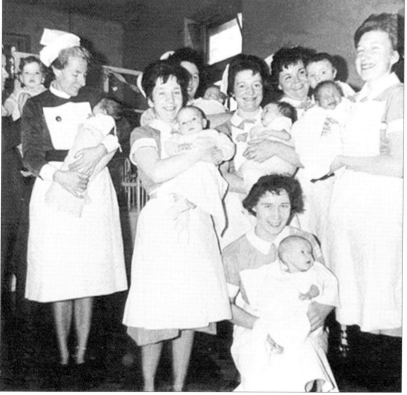

An abundance of babies. The Ward Sister and nurses pose with newborn infants for a publicity shot.

FOUR

Patients' Stories

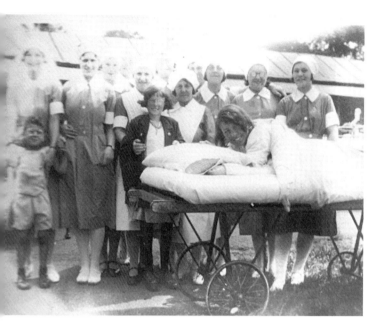

Left: Staff and patients in the grounds of the Orthopaedic Hospital, Hartshill. The hospital was set up in Longfield Cottage by the Cripples Aid Society in 1919, and temporary buildings were added in the 1920s. A new Orthopaedic Hospital opened in 1931.

Centre left: The Open Air Pavilion, Orthopaedic Hospital, Hartshill. Fresh air was regarded as a curative.

Below left: Patients in traction, 1950s. A former patient described this as being 'a modified form of the mediaeval rack' and remembers falling over when he was finally allowed to walk again.

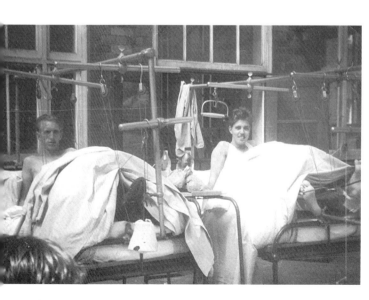

Above: Adult patients and staff in the open air ward at the Orthopaedic Hospital. This photograph is from an album that belonged to Annie Nelmes, a nurse at the hospital.

The gymnasium, Orthopaedic Hospital. A youth is hanging from the top bar of the exercise frame.

Below: Posed photograph in a male ward, *c.*1930s. A patient with a head bandage can be seen sitting in a wheelchair. Many patients spent weeks or months in hospital. 'You just got on with it,' said one.

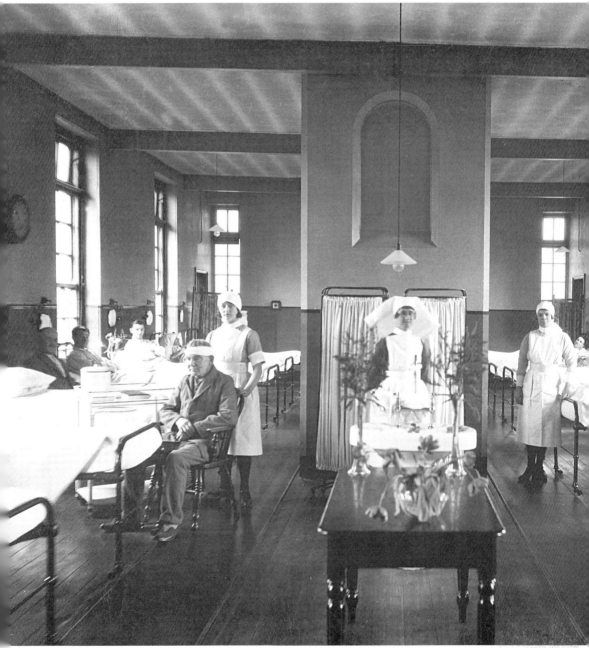

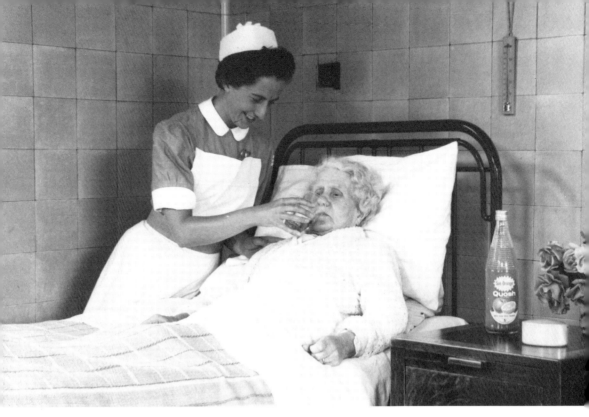

Above: Medicine round, Infirmary Ey Block, 1950s.

In 1942, Edna Elsie Baggaley was admitte to the Infirmary for pioneering heart surge by Dr Clement Price Thomas (who late operated on the King). Her parents we advised that she would not live beyond th age of 12 without surgery. The operatio had been tried out, unsuccessfully, six tim previously. Although she lost weight an nursing staff feared she would die, she mad a full recovery.

Patients and staff outside Ward 9, 1949. Patients often got to know each other quite well, and would be very distressed if someone died after surgery. 'There were some sad times, especially when you've been in for a long time and you get to know people.'

Patients and staff stand in the hospital yard, c.1951. Jean Rowe, from Boothen in Stoke-on-Trent, stands on the far right. She developed pleurisy and tuberculosis when she was seventeen. Admitted to Ward 2 in the Infirmary, she had several operations, developed pneumonia, and spent ten months there.

Above and below: After her long stay in Ward 2, Jean Rowe (now Charsley), was sent to Loggerheads sanatorium to recuperate. She was there for 14 months. 'We used to call it little Switzerland. We had to sleep outdoors. We were under cover in the winter but all the doors were open, and all you had to keep you warm was a hot water bottle.'

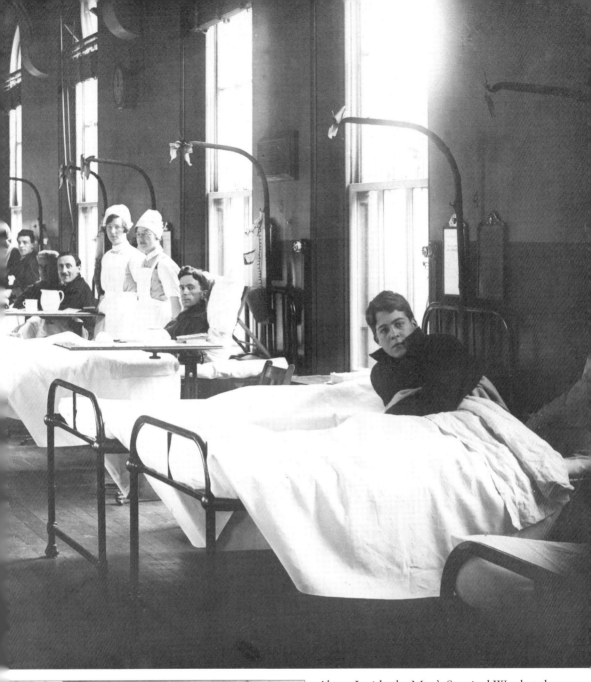

Above: Inside the Men's Surgical Ward at the London Road Hospital, 1930. The hospital was renamed the 'City General' in 1945.

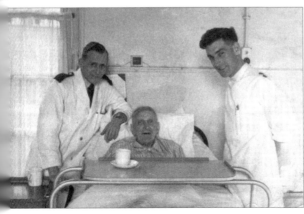

Tom Byatt and a colleague pose with a patient in the Male Ward at the City General Hospital, mid-1950s.

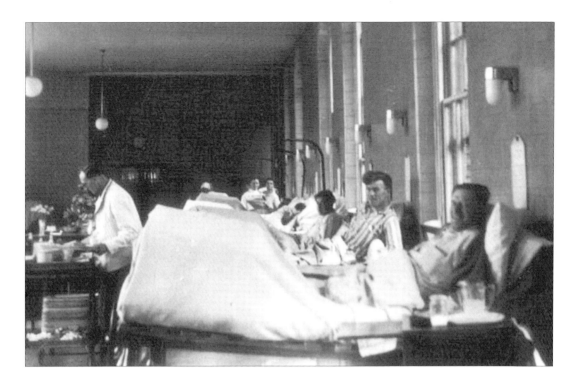

Above: William Edge was admitted to Ward 1 in March 1951 following a serious motorbike accident. He had a badly broken right leg, which the surgeons wanted to amputate. He decided to risk an operation. At one stage during his treatment, maggots were used to clean the wounds. He left hospital after six months and returned home to Martinslow in the Staffordshire Moorlands with a specially made boot and calliper.

Above right: Female patients and staff, outside the Infirmary, mid-1960s. Visiting hours were very restricted and patients had to amuse themselves. A female patient remembers keeping herself busy with reading, knitting and embroidering a tablecloth during a long stay.

Right: Patients in the open air on the verandah, London Road Hospital, 1936. 'You did make friends with some patients,' recalled one nurse. 'There were some lovely people.'

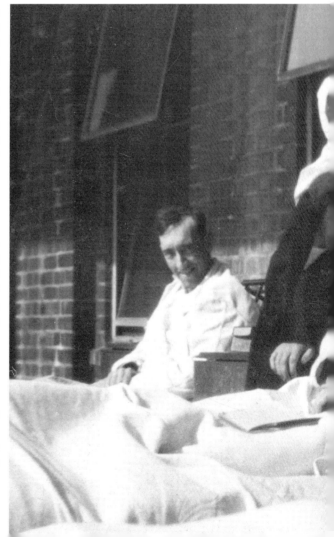

48

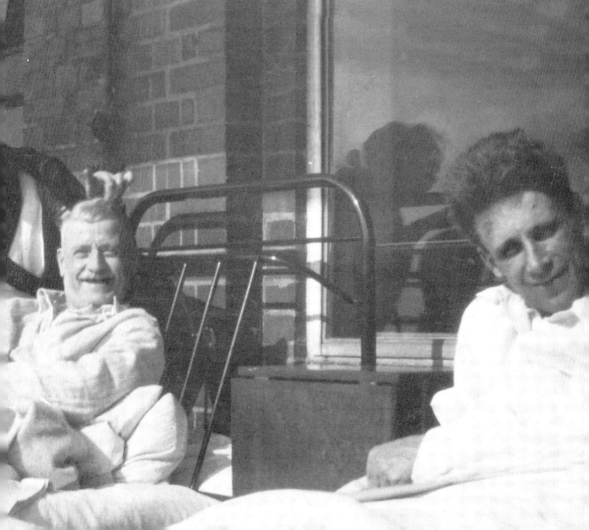

Staff and patients on the balcony of Ward 2, Infirmary, 1958. The ward had beds for gynaecology, thoracic and general surgery patients. A small, six bedded room at the end of the ward opened onto the balcony. Standing in the centre is Mona Boden, who had undergone heart surgery. The young girl in the foreground, a patient of Mr Ramage, had undergone bladder surgery. The ward was on the first floor, above the Male Orthopaedic Ward.

FIVE

'Boys, Girls, Babies, Toddlers'

Nursing staff holding two small children, Orthopaedic Hospital. For many children a stay in hospital was the first time that they had ever left home.

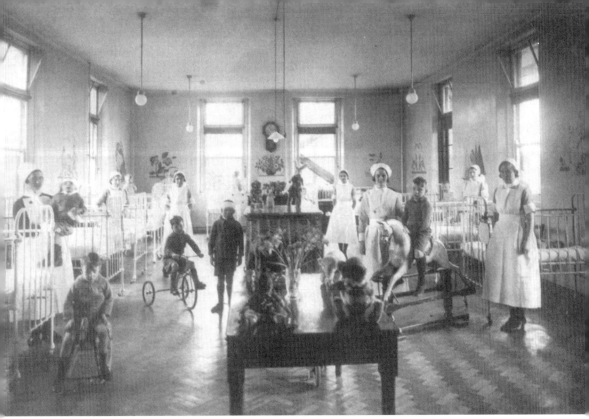

Above: Children's Ward at the City General
Hospital, 1930s. One boy is riding a tricycle,
while another sits on a rocking horse.

Above and right: Nursing staff and young
patients at the Orthopaedic Hospital.

A boy and girl stand on the grass in fron of the Open Air Ward.

The Massage Room at the Orthopaedic Hospital, 1925. Nurses treat children with bone deformities. Casts of children's deformed feet are hanging on the wall. These were used by the hospital cobbler to make corrective footwear for each child.

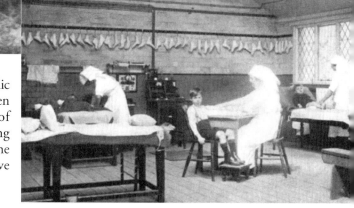

Left: Inside the gym at the Orthopaed Hospital, 1925. Boys hang from the exercise bar under the supervision their nurses.

Below: Children in the Open A Ward pose for the camera. They see remarkably cheerful. 'There was a b verandah outside where the girls use to push us, the lads, in the beds, yo couldn't get out of bed,' recalled a form child patient.

A group of patients and staff from the Cheetham Hospital for Children. Two of the girls are holding tennis rackets. One former child patient remembered being taken for walks to see the animals on the nearby farm.

The staff of the Cheetham Hospital. A former nurse described the children's hospital as 'a big square building divided into four, Boys, Girls, Babies, Toddlers. Simple as that!' It was demolished in 1989.

Below: Young patients enjoy a visit from Uncle Remus, 1940. As children were often in hospital for a long period, visiting hours were restricted and amusements were few, visiting entertainers were enthusiastically received.

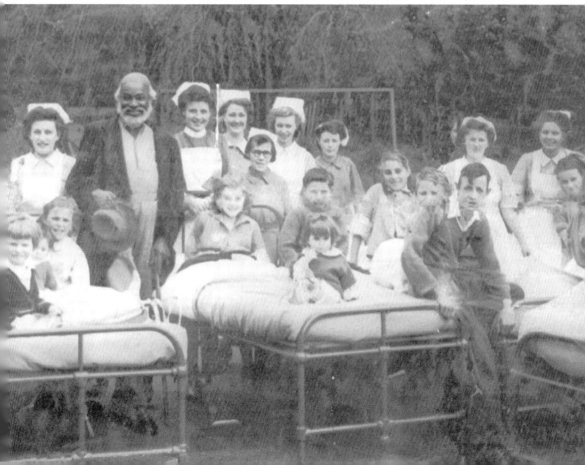

Left: Children are entertained at the Orthopaedic Hospital, September 1946. This photograph was taken while Frederick Cooper (bottom left), was a patient at the Orthopaedic Hospital. Then two years old, he had been born with a dislocated hip which took a couple of years to correct. The boy with his left leg in plaster is John Bannister, who was a patient for about four years and an outpatient for a further seven. Sister Johnson is holding his head up.

Below left: Nursing staff pose with a young patient outside the Male Surgical Ward, 1949. Children were sometimes placed in an adult ward. One patient who was put into Ward 1 as an eight-year-old remembers, 'There was no entertainment, no books for you to read, no radio. You just sat in bed all day.'

Below: Coronation Day in the Infirmary Children's Ward, 2 June 1953. Children wave union jacks for the camera.

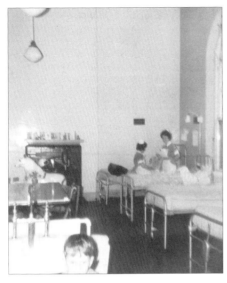

Above: A rocking-horse can be seen at the back of the ward in this informal snapshot. 'I wanted to go on the rocking horse,' said one former patient, 'but I was too small to get on'.

Right: Nurses with a child patient on the Children's Ward, Infirmary, 1962.

Below: Tea time at the Infirmary Children's Ward, 1950. Sister Wales gives encouragement to a young boy.

'The youngest patient on the Male Surgical Ward', 1949. A former child patient remembered, 'There were about five of us children on Ward 1. There were 32 beds in that ward. It was old fashioned. People came in for operations. We saw them come and go. You just got on with life.'

Young patients and their carers in the Children's Ward, August 1950.

Staff Nurse Woodward with a young patient, c.1950. This toddler had been one of the smallest premature babies on the ward.

Children's Ward, 1957. Nurse Joan Wooldridge stands on the far left.

Teresa Woodward presents a doll's house to Christine Knapper, January 1954. Christine was in hospital for her second birthday following an accident on the railway line near her home in Kidsgrove. Among the onlookers are Harold Davies, MP for Leek, and E. Hodgkinson, Chairman of Kidsgrove Council.

Staff Nurse Beadle with a young patient, Patricia Dean, 1959.

SIX

'We worked hard and we played hard'

Top: Nurses pose in their starched caps and freshly laundered white aprons.

Second from top: A group of nurses on the Infirmary balcony. 'Discipline was very strict,' said a retired nurse. 'Hair had to be up and under your cap. No Christian names were allowed on the wards. No nail varnish, no jewellery, no rings, earrings, necklaces.'

An unidentified group of nurses in their uniforms. 'At 10am every day you changed your apron and put on a crisp, white new one,' recalled one former nurse.

'Just off night duty', 1940s. 'On night duty you worked 12-hour shifts, 8pm to 8am, nine nights on, three nights off. Sometimes we actually worked eighteen nights back to back,' said one nurse. 'You were so tired afterwards you often just slept all the time.'

Below: Nurses at the Infirmary, 1939. One nurse who trained at this time remembers using a toothbrush to soften up the edges of her starched pleated cap.

Above: Theatre staff at the Infirmary, 1948. Sister Price (standing, second from left), Kathleen Litherland (centre), Sister Simpson (right) and colleagues.

Below: Nurse Galloway, consultant anaesthetist Dr Isaacson, and Staff Nurse Kathleen Litherland.

Nurses' sitting room in Prince Henry Hall. This was one of the largest rooms in the hospital. There was a piano and dances were held there.

Above: Male nurses in the Infirmary grounds, 1951. 'I first met male nurses in 1948 when I was night sister,' said a Ward Sister. 'They started training after the war at the Infirmary. I think there were two originally. They weren't accepted too well to begin with.'

Kathleen Woodward and colleagues in the Infirmary gardens, 1950s.

Four nurses pose for an informal snapshot outside the Nurses' Home, 1950s.

Above: A group of Orthopaedic Nurses, photographed in around 1952.

Barbara Kontic (*née* Ilsley) began her nursing career at the Infirmary in the 1950s. She was unable to complete her training, as her step-father became ill with cancer and Barbara nursed him for two years. She later nursed at Yarnfield Isolation Hospital and Westcliffe Hospital and worked as the Nurse allocated to Trentham Gardens. She then worked part-time at the Infirmary for a number of years.

Above: Sister Sybil Brown who later emigrated to New Zealand.

Above right: Dr Prabhu, Sister Bose and Sister Tyler, September 1962.

Nurses and auxiliaries, 1966, with Soo Khoo, a nurse from Malaysia (seated, centre).

Above: Presentation of a television to the Infirmary Nurses' Home.

Top right: Nurses watching television, Prince Henry's Hall. A nurse who was resident in the late 1950s remembers that 'there was a black and white television, but half the time it didn't work. It was ever such a small one, so get two or three round it and nobody else could see it.'

Centre right: Two off-duty nurses in one of the bedrooms in the Nurses' Home in the mid-1960s. These had recently been refurbished.

Below right: Sister Burslem relaxes in her room. Note the electric bar fire.

Above: Two nurses off duty, in the Infirmary grounds, 1960s.

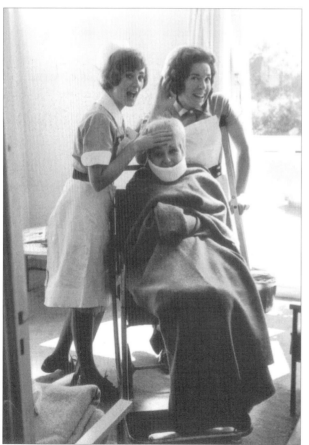

Nurses amuse themselves out of Matron's view. 'You just had to make your own fun,' explained a nurse who trained in the 1960s. 'We were always playing pranks on each other, but it was always clean fun. We were probably little devils, really.' This sequence of photographs is from the collection of Prem and Margaret Seewoosaha.

Broomhandles at dawn.

Two young nurses let off steam in the Infirmary grounds.

'We worked hard and we played hard.' This summary of their working life was repeated by many of the nurses interviewed for *If Wards Could Talk*.

SEVEN

Celebrations … and Setbacks

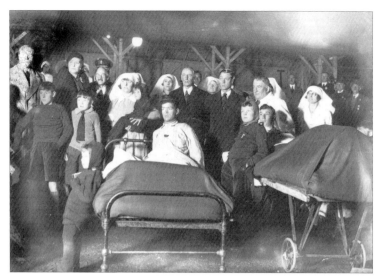

Left: Official opening of the Hartshill Orthopaedic Hospital, 1931. The Prince of Wales (later Edward VIII) poses stiffly for the camera with patients and staff including Dr Mitchell-Smith and Dora Veitch.

Below left: Royal visit to the Infirmary, 5 June 1925. During this visit, King George V laid the Foundation Stone of the New Medical Block and granted 'royal' status to the Infirmary.

Below: The First Infirmary Nurses' League reunion, 1939. Once a year, in summer, Prince Henry Hall was prepared for a reunion of nurses who had trained at the Infirmary. Former students often asked to revisit their old rooms, recalling incidents from student life.

Above: Fred Emerson, Infirmary head porter and mortician, is presented with a silver cigarette case for his part in the rescue of an injured miner at Hanley Deep Pit, 1935. He had volunteered to accompany one of the doctors underground to help with a possible amputation. The miner's leg was trapped but his colleagues managed to free him. Also pictured is E. Fairweather (second left).

Above and below: Bomb damage to Nurses' Home, 1940. The 100-bedroom extension to the Nurses' Home had only just been completed when it was bombed by German aircraft on 29 June. Damage was quite extensive. A large section of the Nurses' Home was wrecked, the new Eye Theatre destroyed and the new medical wards cut off from the main infirmary buildings.

Nurses inspect bomb damage outside the Nurses' Home.

The cost of the damage was estimated at £10,000. During the following month new shelters and blast walls were installed.

Top left: Matron Blakemore cuts the cake at the annual Nurses' League reunion, 1950.

Below left: Nurses' League members seated for the reunion tea, 1950. Matron (standing, far right) looks on. According to a former League member, the day 'was marked by a competitive display of colourful hats'.

Above: The Nurses' League Reunion Organising Committee, 1952.

Right: Invitation to prize presentation, May 1951.

North Staffordshire Royal Infirmary

·—·

Presentation

of

Medals, Prizes & Certificates

TO THE NURSING STAFF

by

SIR ERNEST JOHNSON, J.P.,

(President of the Infirmary, 1927-31, and 1945-48).

on *Thursday, 31st May, 1951,*

at 2-45 p.m.

in the Prince Henry Hall

Chairman — Dr. Charles W. Healey, M.D.

Above: Adult Male Ward at the Infirmary decorate[d] for Coronation Day, 2 June 1953.

ROYAL COLLEGE OF NURSING

STOKE-ON-TRENT BRANCH.

CORONATION

SUMMER FETE

(in aid of the above Branch)

IN THE GROUNDS OF THE
NORTH STAFFORDSHIRE ROYAL INFIRMARY

THURSDAY, JUNE 25th

at 3 p.m.

FANCY STALLS · SIDE SHOWS · PUNCH & JUDY
DONKEY RIDES · COMPETITIONS · ANKLE JUDGING

Entrance Nurses Home
ADMISSION: Adults 1/6 Children 9d.
(including Tea)

M & U Ltd., Newcastle

Left: Flyer for Coronation fête, June 1953. The Stok[e]-on-Trent branch of the Royal College of Nursi[ng] held a fete in the Infirmary grounds to celebrate t[he] coronation.

Above right: A young girl enjoys a pony ride at t[he] Coronation fête watched by members of the organisi[ng] committee in this heavily posed photograph.

Right: Fête Committee members pose behind a sta[ll] 1953. Matron stands in the back row, centre.

Top left: Opening of new operating theatre suite at the Infirmary by Sir Edward Thompson.

Centre left: Ticket for the Royal visit, July 1965.

Below left and above: Princess Margaret opening the new Accident and Emergency department, 1 July 1965. Student nurse Joan Pointon presented a bouquet to her. She recalls: 'I got a brief but close look at the Princess and vividly remember how small she seemed to me – about 5 feet – her beautiful clear blue eyes, the overdone makeup and the fact that she never said 'thank you' for the flowers'.

NORTH STAFFORDSHIRE ROYAL INFIRMARY
STOKE-ON-TRENT

1869   1969

NURSES' LEAGUE
JOURNAL
Centenary Edition

DEO JUVANTE

No. 29   1969

LEAGUE OF TRAINED NURSES 1937 - 1973

You are reminded that the

FINAL RE-UNION

OF LEAGUE MEMBERS

will be held on

Saturday, 28th April, 1973

Above left: Seven Infirmary staff were among the 3,000 nurses from 57 different countries that attended the Congress of the International Council of Nurses in Rome in May 1957. Delegates were received at St Peter's where they 'had a front row position and you could almost have touched the Pope'.

Top right: Cover of *Nurses' League Journal*, 1969. 'We had a very special reunion in the centenary year 1969', recalled League Secretary Kathleen Woodward. 'Lunch was all laid out in Prince Henry Hall, there was a marquee on the lawn, and a service in the chapel with the Bishop of Chester.'

Centre right: Invitation to the final Nurses' League reunion, 1973. The League disbanded following the merger of the Infirmary and the City General although former members continued to meet informally.

Far left: A serious fire devastates the Infirmary laundry roof, c.1973.

Left: Radiographers strike, 1974. Picketing radiographer Joy Adams hands a leaflet to patient Terence Hopley of Cheadle.

Service for nursing staff at Lichfield Cathedral, 1960s.

EIGHT

Christmas on the Wards

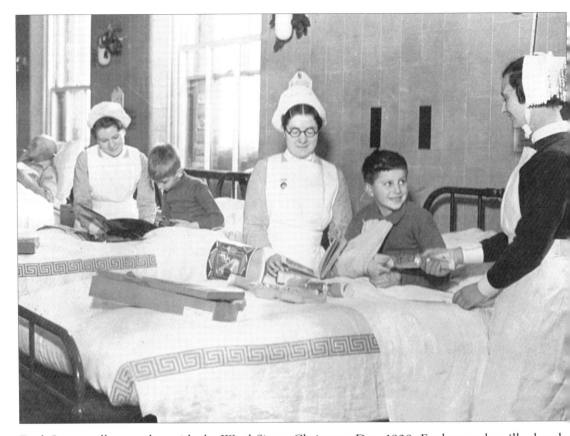

Fred Owen pulls a cracker with the Ward Sister, Christmas Day, 1938. Fred was taken ill when he was eight years old. He had a bone graft on his leg, which led to a succession of further operations. He remembers, 'I was in and out of hospital for four and a half years. The best time was Christmas. The doctors used to be Santa Claus and we had decorations up, but when the war was on that all stopped and if the sirens went, those who could they used to put under the bed. When I went back to school I was twelve and a half.'

Christmas party in the casting room at the Orthopaedic Hospital, 1925.

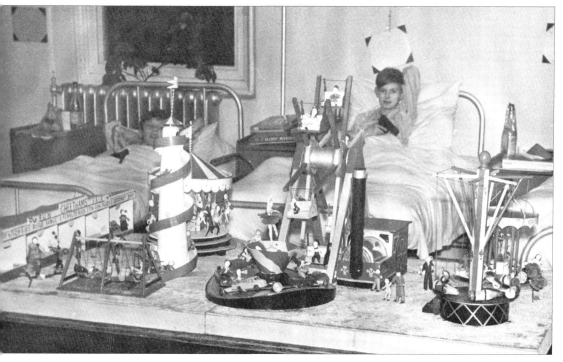

Christmas Day at Cheetham's. Two boys contemplate a display of toys from their beds.

A ward decorated for Christmas. Nobody wants to spend Christmas in hospital, but the nursing staff always made sure that there was a good atmosphere in the wards.

Above: Mr Keates, Registrar, prepares t
serve the turkey in the Henry Johnson Ward
helped by his sons Peter and Jeremy.

Mr Grocott, Consultant Plastic Surgeo
carves the turkey for patients in the Albe
Ward, *c.*1962. A former nurse recalle
'Whoever was the senior consultant on o
ward always used to come in on Christm
day and carve the turkey. I don't know wh
drove him there because he was usually
bit wobbly'.

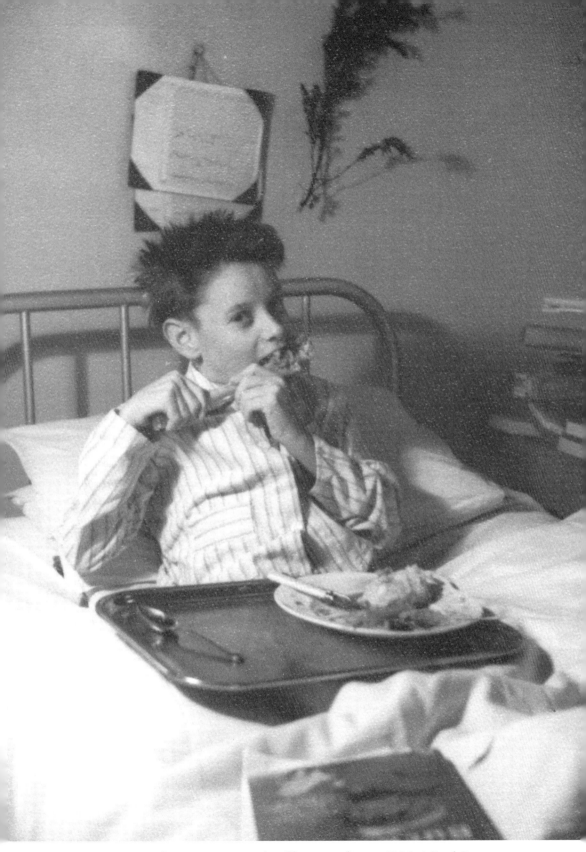

A young patient, Neil Patterson, enjoys his Christmas dinner, 1936. A Buck Jones cowboy annual is lying at the foot of the bed.

Above: Sister Burslem and colleagues pose with Christmas table-top decorations, early 1950s. 'In the weeks before Christmas we were busy planning decorations for the wards,' said a former Ward Sister. 'There would be a large decorated tree with suitable toys and decorations in the children's ward and one in the main entrance hall.'

Sister Jones and colleagues stand in front of a decorated tree in Ward 2 on Christmas Day 1957. 'On Christmas Eve we used to go carol singing round the wards with lanterns and we used to turn our capes inside out', recalled one nurse.

Above: Sisters Woodward and Burslem (centre) and colleagues with Christmas decorations in the Henry Johnson Ward, 1950s.

Left: Staff Nurse Tom Byatt and a Ward Sister pose by the Christmas tree in a ward at the City General Hospital, *c.*1954.

Boxing Day on Ward 2 at the Infirmary, 1958. Friends and relatives were invited to enjoy a cup of tea and a mince pie in the ward during the afternoon. The two small boys are the nephews of Staff Nurse Audrey Thornton (right).

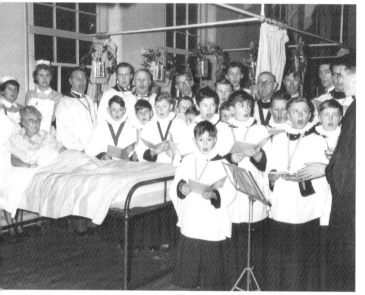

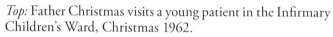

Top: Father Christmas visits a young patient in the Infirmary Children's Ward, Christmas 1962.

Above: Members of Bucknall St Mary's Church Choir sing for patients in Ward 2, Christmas 1960.

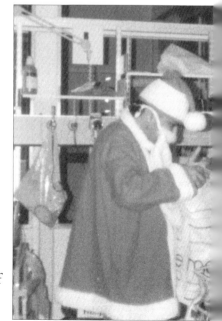

Above right: Santa Claus arrives at a party held for children of Neonatal Unit staff, 1970s.

Right: Santa Claus visits the Neonatal Unit, 1990s.

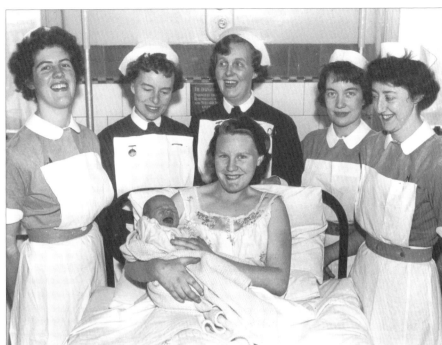

Above: A Christmas baby. Mrs Jean Clowes and her baby, December 1961. Another mother remembered, 'My baby boy was the last one born on Christmas Day. There had been a wonderful Christmas Dinner but I felt quite ill and ate nothing till after I had given birth. We were really well looked after.'

Mrs Mavis Axon and her Christmas baby, Nicholas, 1961. A great fuss was made of babies born at Christmas.

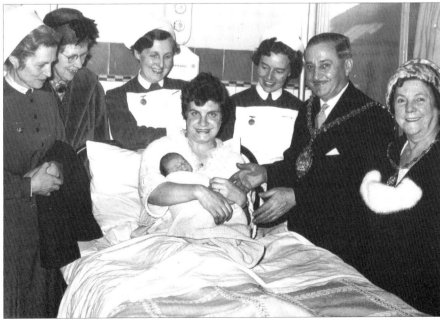

Doctors' Office Party, Christmas 1959. Mr Zinck, Staff Nurse Baines, Staff Nurse Wooldridge, and Sister Talley enjoy the festive spirit.

Christmas Day on the Albert Ward, Infirmary, c.1962. Dr Dasgupta and Sister Barbara Beeston stand on the far right.

Staff, family and friends celebrate Boxing Day, 1960s. The Cadman children are in the foreground.

Mauritius-born male nurse Prem Seewoosaha as Santa Claus.

Prem Seewoosaha and 'Santa Claus' in the ward office, decorated
for Christmas.

Nursing and medical staff let their hair down at an Infirmary Christmas party.

Above: Hospital staff dressed up for the Christmas Ball, 1950s.

Ticket for the Christmas Dance, 1954.

THE ANENCEPHALICS ANONYMOUS

present

The Christmas Show
1961

❧

10th and 11th JANUARY, 1961

Top left: Matron's Christmas Ball, mid-1950s. 'Matron had an annual dance,' recalls one former nurse. 'We had a big band, and you could invite boyfriends, but the bedrooms were out of bounds to visitors. No boyfriends were allowed in bedrooms.'

Top centre: Cover of programme for the Christmas show, 1961. This featured the duet of Lavage and Sink, This Is Your Knife, and Casualty Candid Camera.

Below left: Many nurses remember the Christmas pantomime in Prince Henry Hall. 'Many of the staff took part, sisters, nurses, doctors, cleaners, anyone who was interested in taking part did. It was always enjoyable, it was always a laugh.'

Above: Pantomime horse and other characters. The Nurses' Home Sister explained that 'great sliding doors in the hall were drawn apart to enable a stage and seating for the audience to be erected. The concert, so enjoyable, was produced three or four times. Quite a deal of talent was shown.'

Christmas show, with assorted sheriffs and minstrels. 'I was the sheriff in a Christmas show,' said Sister Woodward. 'Matron came to see our dress rehearsal and decided we were absolutely hopeless and should not go on. However, we did go on and we were a great success.'

Top right: 'Snow White and three dwarves' at a Neo-Natal Unit Christmas party, late 1980s.

Centre and bottom right: New Year's Eve celebrations at the Neonatal Unit, 1986.

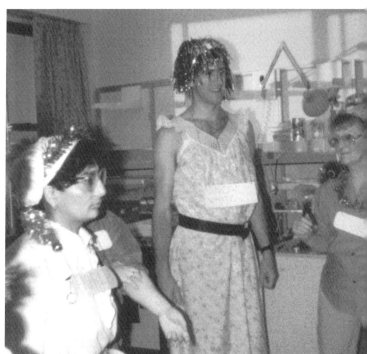

109

Dr Tiwari and a fellow medic indulge themselves in time-honoured fashion at a staff Christmas party at the Infirmary.

NINE

Hospital Life, Hospital Lives

Above: Nurses' League charabanc outing. The Nurses' League arranged outings for its members. Trips included visits to country houses such as Haddon Hall and a guided tour of the Boots factory at Nottingham, where the nurses saw medicines being made.

Right: Nurses' outing to Liverpool. Infirmary nurses pose by the docks.

Left: City General Hospital nurses on holiday at Butlin's, Skegness. They are wearing identical dresses made with lining fabric 'obtained' from Enderley Mills, Newcastle-under-Lyme. Elsie Elizabeth Knight is third from left.

Top left: Elsie Elizabeth Knight and friends on holiday in Skegness

Top right: Infirmary nursing students Easter Parade, 1954

Right: Concert organised by nursing students on behalf of the World Refugee Fund.

Infirmary holiday pass made out to Staff Nurse Wooldridge, 1959. These passes were issued by the Matron.

Top left: Nurses display their hula skirts at the Royal Infirmary concert, January 1954.

⟵ "OUR SET"

Left: Nurses take a bow at the Hospital show. These were very amusing, remembered one nurse, 'a little bit near the knuckle but hilarious. The script and everything was actually written by the staff. Quite a few of them had a really good sense of humour.'

Top right: Brenda Powner, Joan Spencer and Cynthia Hulme perform a sketch at the Infirmary concert, *c.*1958. Shows were famous for puns and references to consultants. A typical example: 'We would like to apologise for the lameness of the show. Perhaps Orthopaedics could do something about it.'

Second from top: Pat Johnson and colleagues rehearse for a hospital show routine.

Top left: Sister Kathleen Woodward sits among daffodils outside the Infirmary Nurses' Home, 1950s.

Left: The Infirmary's young nurses were not immune from the British folk boom of the 1960s. One wrote in the student magazine that 'hearing Cyril Tawney singing the Oggy Man does to me what Cliff Richard singing one of his romantic ballads does to most girls (funny women!)'.

Above: Sisters Hazeldine and Clarke picnicking at Barlaston Downs, *c.*1957. They were both night sisters at the time. Barlaston Downs was a popular place for a family day out.

Above: Infirmary nurses demonstrate their bowling skills, 1953.

Top right: Competitors in the Durose Cup inter-hospital tennis tournament. On the left representing the Infirmary are Miss J. Hobson and Mr A. Furnival. There were tennis courts in the hospital grounds.

Centre right: The Central Outpatients Ladies Football team receive the Soroptimists 'cut-out cup', 1972. The team included medical, technical, physio-therapy and clerical staff.

Below right: The Ladies and Junior Doctors Football teams go head to head. The ladies also played against a consultants' team. Vivienne Clements broke her ankle during the match in a collision with a consultant. The ladies team are wearing Stoke City training tops.

Above: Third-year student nurses dressed up for a social event at The Cristal, Newcastle-under-Lyme, *c.*1967. 'Although nursing was hard work, we had a social life as well,' recalled one nurse who trained at this time. 'We all lived in at the hospital, so we made our own social pastimes. We went to dances at Trentham, the Castle in Newcastle, the Cristal, the Queen's.'

Top left: Dental Department five-a-side football team, 1974

Centre left: Hospital ladies five-a-side Football team at Keele University, where they were cup winners in a local tournament.

Below left: Members of the Neonatal team stage a performance at staff leaving party, with Dr Spencer in the background.

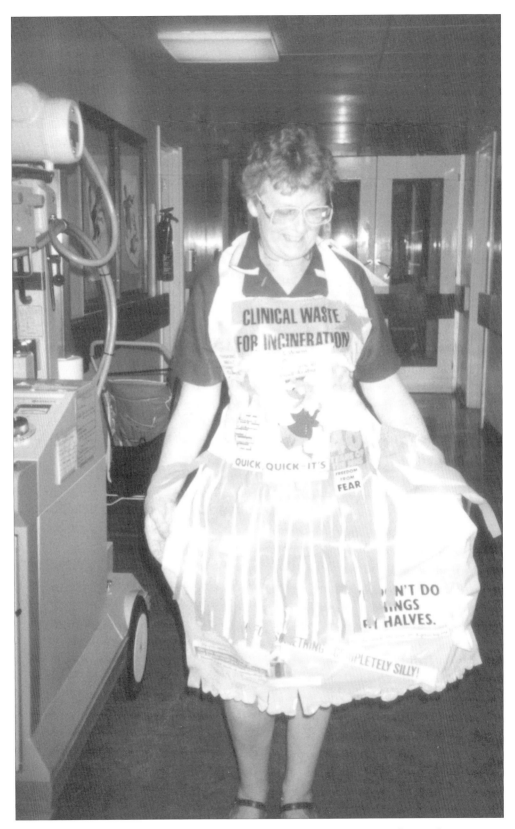

Jean Allen displays her apron at a staff leaving party in the Neonatal Unit: 'A warm welcome awaits you in Saudi Arabia.'

bove: The Special Children's Baby Unit
·am provide 'Milk-maids of honour' at
Michelle Ball's wedding. Olive Kelsall and
·an Oliver hold a 'good luck' banner.

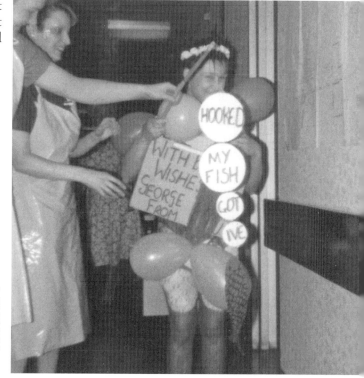

bride-to-be undergoes a ritual pre-
·dding 'wetting' session at the Special
·ildren's Baby Unit. 'We used to fill
·inges up to squirt the bride to be. They all
·me prepared with a change of underwear,'
·alls a former nursery nurse.

Above: Grace Harrison, Infirmary Queen. Before the creation of the NHS a Carnival of Queens was held at Hanley Park during the first week in August in aid of the area's voluntary hospitals. Accompanying the Queen were jazz bands, dancing troupes, a horse parade, and decorated vehicles. The day ended with a fireworks display. Each year one Queen was chosen to be the Infirmary Queen and given collecting box for her year of office.

Above: Nurses' League bring
and buy sale, 1950s. 'We were
always raising funds for this,
that and the other,' recalled
the League Secretary.

Right: In 1977 City General
nurses took part in a crazy
football competition to raise
money for ECG machines.
Stoke City players acted as
linesmen and Geoff Hurst
refereed. Feeling sorry for the
nurses, who were being beaten
by the doctors, he kicked the
ball into the net for them.
Sister Mobbs is wearing a
dark shirt.

Left: Gladys Jackson, Hartshill
Queen and her attendants,
1937. This photograph was
taken on the green at the
corner of the Avenue and
Albany Road.

Staff take part in a sponsored run around the perimeter of Central Outpatients, 20 May 1974.

Radio Stoke presenter, Mel Scholes, presents a fundraising cheque to Ward Sister Janet Gaunt of the Burns Unit, Ward 5, at Bailey's Nightclub in Longton, 1974. Adrian Luckhurst, Charles Lansley and Vivienne Clements look on.

Fundraiser Ron Alcock poses with the Body Scanner Appeal car, with Nurse Diane Martin of Ward 18 and Phyllis Ford, Appeal Secretary, February 1981.

Cheadle youth club members raised money for the appeal from a disco. Superintendent Gordon Toft presents the proceeds to Ron Alcock.

Stoke & District
CANCER EQUIPMENT APPEAL
FOR A
BODY SCANNER

REG. CHARITY No. 600040

PATRON
KEN DODD

PLEASE HELP US
TO BUY TIME
IT COULD BE YOURS

DONATIONS, GIFTS, MEMORIALS.

To The Hon. Treasurer

MR. B. STINTON.

c/o LLOYDS BANK LTD.

Church St, Stoke-on-Trent.

Enquiries to
The Hon. Secretary,
Mrs. P. Ford. Tel: 562653

STOKE DISTRICT CANCER EQUIPMENT
APPEAL - BODY SCANNER

HELP US TO BUY TIME – IT COULD BE YOURS

Recipe Competition-Dinner Dance

MENU

Crest Hotel
Newcastle-under-Lyme
Thursday, October 30th. 1980

Left: Poster for Body Scanner Appeal event with Ken Dodd.

Above top: Fundraiser Ron Alcock presents a ceramic jester to Appeal Patron Ken Dodd.

Above: Cover of menu for fundraising meal at the Crest Hotel, 1980.

Above: Morris Minor Rally, 1989. The Infirmary's League of Friends organised several fundraising events with the local branch of the Morris Minor club. As well as a rally, these included activities such as a hospital bed push race, blind-fold driving and a tug-of-war against a team from the police.

Below: Hospital bed-pushing competition in the Infirmary grounds, 1991.

Right: Poster for the Building Blocks appeal, 1990. This high profile campaign raised money for a new Child Development Centre.

Child Development Centre

BUILDING BLOCKS APPEAL 1990

North Staffordshire Hospital Children's Trust
Registered No. 701338

Above: Carte de visite showing Hilda Annie Wilcox, *c.*1918. Hilda Wilcox trained at the Infirmary from 1915 to 1918, when she became a staff nurse. She then trained as a midwife. The Matron described her as 'a capable and kindly nurse, painstaking and conscientious, who works well with others and is of high moral character'.

Above right: Hilda (Wilcox) Woolliscroft at Nurses' League reunion, 1950s. During the 1930s Hilda Wilcox worked at the Thomas Twyford Infants Welfare Centre in Hanley. She left in 1939 and later married. In her retirement she played a prominent role in the Nurses' League, serving for many years as Vice-President.

Right: Jane MacMaster, Matron at the Infirmary, 1905-31. She was remembered as 'an organiser and disciplinarian, but, above all, for her deep concern for the welfare of patients and nursing-staff alike'. During her time the Infirmary saw great changes, with the addition of a Children's Ward, new Outpatients' Department, and Pathological Laboratory. She was awarded the Royal Red Cross for her services during the 1914-18 War, when the Infirmary cared for sick and wounded servicemen.

Medical staff, North Staffordshire Royal Infirmary, 1935. The consultants are shown wearing academic dress.

Below: Medical staff and hospital chaplain standing at the main entrance of the Infirmary, 1950s. As in 1935, there are only two female faces.

Eva Blakemore, Matron at the Infirmary, 1930-50. She played an important role in ensuring the smooth transition of the Infirmary from a voluntary hospital to part of the new National Health Service. She died in Hove, Sussex, in 1965. A colleague recalled her as a 'great Matron who, like Florence Nightingale, would stop at nothing for the benefit of the Infirmary, and in cases of emergency would turn up her sleeves and work in the ward with the nurses'. She was often accompanied by her dog.

Vera Corbishley, June 1940. Vera Corbishley trained at the infirmary from 1937 to 1940, after spending two years at Bucknall Fever Hospital. She remembers seeing a picture of a district nurse when she was at school and deciding that was what she wanted to be. When she arrived at the Infirmary, she went straight onto the wards, and also gained experience in the operating theatre, out patients and casualty. She was delighted when she qualified and could wear the Infirmary badge, with its motto Deo Juvante ('With God's help'). 'I treasured my badge,' she said. 'It had been my dream to acquire that badge.' She later worked as a district midwife in Longport and Middleport and as a nurse at the Haywood Hospital, before returning briefly to the Infirmary. She then worked as a district nurse until she married.

Above left: Matron E.M. Smith succeeded Eva Blakemore in September 1950.

Above right: Matron E.M. Tomkinson. According to one of her night sisters, 'She knew exactly what was happening in all the wards. We had to report every morning on our wards. If a patient had a bedsore, she would ask, "Why has she got a bedsore, sister? Has she not been turned over?" You had to explain.'

Right: John Steven Ramage, NSRI Consultant Surgeon 1935-1964. Originally appointed House Surgeon in 1924, Mr Ramage was famous for his aphorisms, such as 'the gentleness of touch is the hall-mark of the good surgeon'. His skill as a surgeon was widely acknowledged and he was open to new clinical ideas. If some of the nursing staff found him 'difficult', they also had genuine affection for him.

Below: Nurses' League Committee with Sister K. Woodward (Secretary), Miss E. Blakemore (President), Matron Tomkinson (Chairman) and Mrs Woolliscroft (Vice-President).

Top right: Elizabeth Logan, Infirmary Matron 1965-9. Formerly Assistant Matron at Birmingham's General Hospital, she later became Chief Nursing Officer at York Hospital.

Below right: Mr Keates, registrar for Consultant Gynaecologist Mr Duthie. A patient remembered him as having 'a very serious face, he rarely smiled, but he was very kind and would always stop for a chat.'

Left: Kathleen Woodward was born in 1921 and grew up in Newcastle-under-Lyme, where she attended the Orme Girls School. Although her parents did not encourage her career choice, she was determined to become a nurse. She trained during wartime from 1940-3 and remembers sleeping on a mattress in the lecture room. She recalls that the friends she made stuck together as a set. She was a Sister on the Henry Johnson Ward (Gynaecology and Maternity) for 25 years. She became Secretary of the Nurses' League when Matron informed her that she was 'volunteering'. She carried out this role enthusiastically and assiduously for many years.

Right: Staff Nurse J. Benbow, North Staffordshire Royal Infirmary, 1953.

Opposite: Sister R.A. Greally, Theatre Superintendent, City General Hospital. 'Rose Anne Greally was an Irish Roman Catholic lady,' said one of her juniors. 'She had standards. Whatever you used in theatre had a place. You didn't just put it away anywhere. You put it in that place. And she would say, "If you need that in an emergency, you need to be able to put your hand out and it is there." And my life is still like that now. I just can't be untidy because that's not how I was trained.'

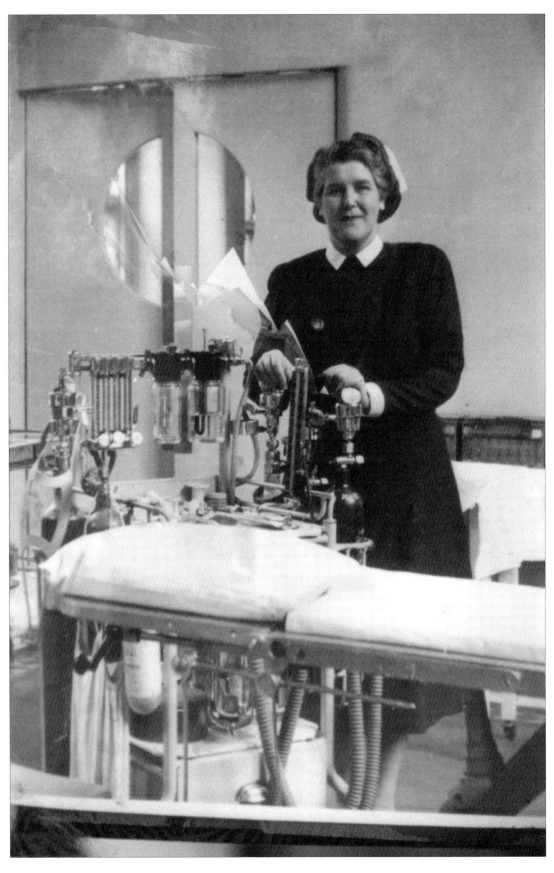

139

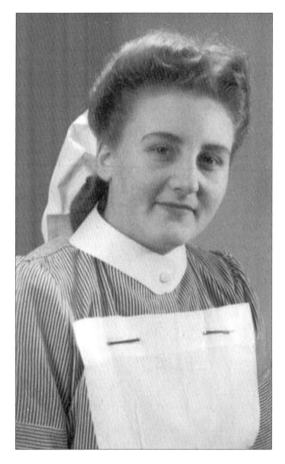

Above left: Elsie Elizabeth Knight was a silv medallist at the City General. Her fiancé used come to meet her from work. Once, when the nurs were running late, he was helping them to make son porridge, when news came that Matron was on h way. He hid in the broom cupboard until she h: left. She later emigrated to Australia, where she r; a nursing home in Adelaide. She died in 2008.

Above right: Erma Clarke (later Taylor) off-du 1950s. Erma was born at St Patrick's, Christchurc in Barbados in 1930. Her father kept a gener store. She left school at 13 and set sail for the UK September 1949. The voyage took two weeks and s arrived at the Infirmary in October. She recalls tl 'everything was grey, there wasn't a lot of colour'. first, she worked as an auxiliary, living in a wood hut in the hospital grounds. She remembers bei woken one night that first winter by the night por to see snow falling for the first time in her life. was a miracle,' she said.

Above: Peggy Grocott, in uniform at her home in Marina Drive, May Bank, 1953. Peggy trained at the City General but did not complete the course. She enjoyed the work, particularly in the Children's Ward, but found hospital discipline stressful.

Twin sisters Joan and Janet Wooldridge on the lawn behind the Nurses' Home, 1956. The twins both trained at the same time. When they were young children, their father became critically ill. Joan was inspired by the quality of care he received to become a nurse herself. After qualifying as a SRN in 1959, she trained as a midwife. She spent 40 years in the nursing profession as a Midwife, District Nursing Sister and a Health Visitor.

Above: Pauline Dawson outside the Nurses' Home. Born in Stoke-on-Trent in 1942, Pauline was the oldest of seven children. She wanted to be a nurse from a very young age, and began pre-nursing training at the Elms Technical College when she was fifteen. She later married a doctor, Suhas Das Gupta, despite a warning from Matron that he was 'a ship passing in the night'.

Right: Ann Tyler in staff nurse's uniform, 1958. After she qualified as a nurse, Ann trained as a Midwife and then returned to the Infirmary as a Night Sister. She remembers living in the Nurses' Home in the 1950s. 'The bedroom was just basic, iron bedstead, flock mattress, wardrobe, dressing table, chair. And we had communal washing facilities, with about five sinks all in a row, and there was a large iron bath, which you really needed to step on to get into it, down the corridor from my room.'

Joan Pointon as a student nurse. When Princess Margaret opened the new Central Outpatients Department and the Accident Unit in July 1965, Joan presented her with a bouquet of flowers. She remembers being called into Matron's office. 'This usually meant a reprimand for some misdemeanour but I couldn't recall having done anything wrong. On entering her office, knees knocking, she greeted me with a reassuring smile and informed me that my name had been "pulled out of the hat" to present H.R.H. Princess Margaret with a bouquet during her visit. For once in my life I remember being momentarily speechless.'

ill Berrisford, City General Hospital, '64. On qualification Gill Berrisford orked in theatre as a Staff Nurse, went to do midwifery training and eventually came a District Nurse. Her first pression of the Nurses' Home was that was like entering a nunnery'. She recalls at Matron Brown 'could see mascara at nillion miles. She would bellow down e corridor, "Nurse, get that eye lacquer 'your eyes immediately". And the length your skirt had to be 10 inches from the or. If you turned it up on the quiet you re in deep trouble because she would get ape measure out and physically measure w far off the floor it was.'

Caricature of Dr Alun Davies. Born in Monmouthshire Alun Davies trained at Cambridge University an London. He became an anaesthetist at the City Genera where there were a number of younger consultants wh had gained experience as anaesthetists during the wa He arrived in 1962 during a very bad winter and wa astonished to see so many oxygen tents in the medica wards. He soon discovered that the city had its ow particular health problems and heard it said that 'if yo could give an anaesthetic in Stoke-on-Trent, you coul do it anywhere.' He remembers that there was a 'goo co-operative spirit at the City General'. Dr Davies h. a passion for medical history and in 2006 published history of the North Staffordshire Infirmary.

Below: Group photograph of district nurses. In 196 Tom Byatt became Newcastle-under-Lyme's first ma District Nurse on a salary of £725 a year.

Originally from Longton, James Wilkinson worked first as a porter at the Infirmary, then as a Ward Orderly at the Orthopaedic Hospital before eventually being accepted for SRN training in 1961. He was one of four male students in a class of twenty-four. He particularly enjoyed working on the Children's Ward, Orthopaedics, and Ward 17, which 'was really busy, patients being admitted at all hours as Emergencies'. He left in 1966 to undertake Orthopaedic training in Birmingham and retired from the NHS in 2008 after 50 years' service.

Wenche Lally was born in 1948 within the Arctic Circle, in Honningsvåg on the North Cape in Northern Norway. Her father was a fisherman and she can remember seeing Sami reindeer swimming across the fjord as a child. She first came to England as a 16-year-old when her sister married an RAF serviceman. She trained at the Infirmary as a State Enrolled Nurse. She then started midwifery training but moved on to special care. She left in 1976 to have a baby, but returned to nursing two years later. In 1984 she took a neonatal intensive care course and became a Senior SEN. She continued to nurse babies in intensive care until she retired in 2008. She remembers first ventilator being installed in the unit and saw great improvements to the care of sick and premature babies.

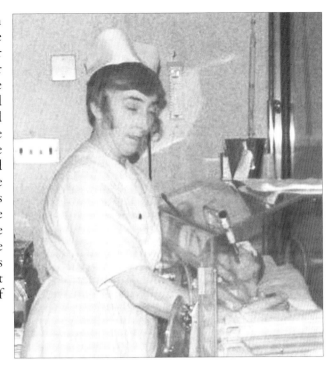

Soo Khoo, Prem Seewoosaha and friend. Born in Mauritius in 1940, Prem Seewoosaha was the first child in his family to go to secondary school. He wanted to become a doctor but his family could not afford a university education. He answered an NHS recruitment advert in the local paper and came to England to train as a nurse. After 29 days at sea and a land journey across France, he arrived in London where he was put on a train to Market Drayton. He worked for two years at the chest hospital in Loggerheads then moved to the Infirmary for general training. At first he was confused by the local dialect. He remembers that on his first morning, a nurse asked him "Could you fetch a bucket, duck?" What was a 'bucketduck'?

Margaret Seewoosaha (right) and friends. Born in Etruria in 1944, Margaret Hopkinson met Prem during her second year as a nursing student. On their first date they saw 'Zulu' at the cinema in Newcastle followed by 'a meal at the only Indian restaurant in Newcastle and that's how it started'. She went back to nursing after her first child was born, initially working one night a week for £14.99.

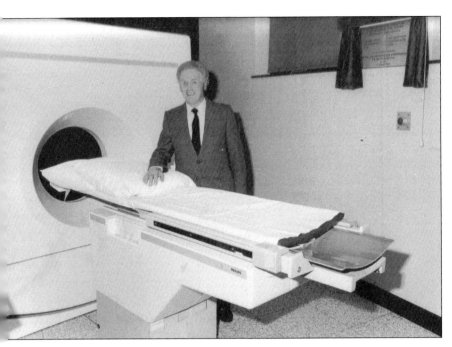

on Alcock, a supervisor at the Creda factory at Blythe Bridge, became involved in
ospital fundraising after he heard Ken Dodd on the radio asking people to help
ith the body-scanner appeal. He set up a Cheadle Branch, and recruited local
ops, pubs and businesses to the campaign. Sponsored events included tug-o-
ars, pub quizzes, discos and a star-studded show at Jollies nightclub in Longton.
e Cheadle campaign raised £26,500 for the scanner. When the equipment was
mmissioned, Ron recalled, 'It was the greatest moment of my life. The scanner
as a Phillips, the best one going.'

adiotherapy
epartment staff
otograph, 1964.

Sisters, Charge Nurses and Departmental Heads. North Staffordshire
Royal Infirmary, 1969.

Radiography Department Staff, March 1989.

Tom Rhodes and colleagues, with LINAC (a high energy X-Ray machine used for treatment of cancers by Radiation Therapy) 1987. Tom Rhodes grew up in Tunstall and Burslem. His mother worked at the hospital as an orderly. He passed the entrance exam to become a police cadet but failed the medical because of poor eyesight. He then applied to train as a radiographer, was successful, and worked in the department until 1994.

Index